Welcome
to
SECRET STREET !

Louisa Campbell

Secret Street

LOUISA CAMPBELL

PENNY DROP
PRESS

A CIP catalogue record for this book is available from the British Library.

First Printing, 2024

Penny Drop Press, Tunbridge Wells, UK

For anyone who carries a secret

Content Indicator

Some people may find some chapters in *Secret Street* distressing to read.

Contents

Royal Tunbridge Wells

Royal Tunbridge Wells commuters stand shiny-shoed on Platform One, waiting for the 7.39 to Charing Cross.

Opposite the station's elegant, canopied entrance, in the multistory car park, a shivering ex-serviceman shifts in his sleeping bag and reaches for his roll-ups.

Mussel shells and a pink-labelled empty Prosecco bottle skulk beneath a High Street wooden bench.

Up the hill in Secret Street, an eighty-year-old gardener oils his bicycle chain. An accountant gulps hot, strong coffee after a sleepless night. A pâtissière in an oversized pink jumper double-checks the calories on a Marks and Spencer fat-free strawberry yoghurt. An addict in a rehab unit crosses through another square on his calendar. A publican daydreams of the Blue Mountains as he carries a clinking crate of Schweppes bottles up from the cellar. A lonely woman in a white nightdress sighs, and stares into an empty oak wardrobe. A prisoner on parole hears the rattle-clank of a guard's keys, then – as it dawns on him he was dreaming – exhales.

Secret Street is waking up.

***

1632. *The water commonly known here amongft us by the name of Tunbridge Water, are two fmall Springs contiguous together, about fome four miles Southward from the town of Tunbridge in Kent from which they have their name, as being the neareft Towne in Kent to them. They are feated in a valley compaffed about with ftony hills, fo barren, that there groweth nothing but heath upon the fame. Juft there doe Kent and Suffex meete, and one may with lefs than half a breath run from thofe Springs into Suffex.* (A Treatise of the Nature and Vertues of Tunbridge Water. Together with an enumeration of the chiefest diseases, which it is good for, and against which it may be used, and the manner and order of taking it, by Dr. of Physick, Lodwick Rowzee of Ashford.)

They come to take the health-restoring waters on the Pantiles. Beau Nash with his frills and curls. Queen Henrietta Maria, in silk and pearls. A swirl of dukes, earls, and dandies. Tunbridge becomes Tunbridge Wells. Up from the heathland spring lodging houses, taverns, a church. Bowling, betting, promenading. Horse racing on the Commons. (It is said nowadays if you walk there at night, you can hear the echo of hooves.) The future Queen Victoria rides her donkey, Flower, in Church Street.

1820. Detached individually-designed Regency villas *...set in a pleasing area of Arcadian parkland.* Grade II listed town houses. *PRIVATE ESTATE.* White stucco and Corinthian pillars. Blowsy balustraded balconies. Porticoes. *Please respect our privacy.*

1909. King George recalls his dear Grandmamma riding her donkey. He calls for the Letters Patent. An inky flourish, a splot of wax, a stamp of a seal, and Tunbridge Wells becomes Royal.

1950s. Banished to the outskirts, know-your-place council houses. Later, white vans. A waft of cannabis smoke that smells like wild garlic.

1970s. Whippersnapper executive estates. Gated. *Residents Only.*

2020s. The Pantiles. White Doric columns. Sankey's Seafood and Champagne Bar, with outside seating draped in sheepskin beneath a white gazebo. *Contemporary British Art.* A stylish woman formed of metal leaf on canvas stares out from the gallery window, mouth slightly open – £2950. A boutique for pampered pooches sells Harris Tweed Collection collars. Objects d'art. *Please press the bell to enter and we will be with you in a moment.*

High Street. Fine Ground coffee, charming mismatched crockery, leaf tea in China teapots, icing-dusted pastries. *The Telegraph Top 50 Best Boutiques in the UK.* Bespoke furnishings. *CCTV IMAGES ARE BEING RECORDED IN THIS STORE.* Corinthian Gold wallpaper ...*matched to a paper from the clock tower at Hampton Court Palace* – £102 a roll.

As they headed off to work in the massage parlour, three Thai girls were caught scrambling out from a downstairs window of the boarded-up pub in Camden Road, where they are believed to have been squatting. (*Tunbridge Wells Herald*, August 2021)

Patek Philippe. Cartier. *The home of fine diamonds.* Lozenge cut, Asscher cut. ('Look at them sparkle!') Security guard – short back and sides, black wool coat, silk tie, black leather gloves, earpiece. ('If you have to ask, you can't afford it.') Dior, Armani, Versace. Longchamp. Fulton umbrellas, *By appointment to Her Majesty Queen Elizabeth II.*

Recent data from the Office of National Statistics reveals Tunbridge Wells is the most unhappy place in Kent, and the fifth most unhappy place in Britain. (The Kent Bugle, November 2022)

11 Secret Street – Araminta Cavendish

The morning sun peeps tentatively in through the etched glass in the front door of No. 11 Secret Street, as if wondering whether it's safe to rise. Araminta Cavendish – known to everyone but herself as "Minty" – tries not to notice the silver-framed wedding photo on the hall cabinet, picks up her Harrod's shopping bag, heavy with neat stacks of identical letters, and opens the door. It's so early, and quiet, it seems to Araminta that at this moment she's barely a ghost of herself, and if she wanted, she could start again as someone new, even now at this burdensome age of eighty-two, which seems to have caught her unawares.

As she closes the door behind her, Araminta stops for a moment to admire its smart royal blue paint, the polished brass knocker and matching number eleven glinting in the beam from the outdoor wall light. She loves her house, with its four storeys, ground floor bay windows, warm, red-brick walls and, on the upper floors, sash windows beneath a gabled roof, topped with an ornate fascia and a pretty wooden finial. She loves her street with its red pavements made of timeworn pressed clay bricks that somehow remind her of Plasticine. The houses in Secret Street were all more or less built the same, with small front gardens and much bigger back ones. Some residents have little velvety lawns at the front, as does Araminta's; others hand-cut patios or cobbles showing off nice stone pots and planters, and edged with white picket fences or low stone walls. A gust of chilly air ruffles her dyed blond hair. She sweeps a stray lock back up into her French pleat and buttons up her cream wool winter coat as she steps onto the pavement. She says hello to a woman in an emerald green duffle coat, walking a Staffordshire bull terrier. Her 'hello' seems to clang like a bell and hang in the air above her as she realises this is the first time she's heard her voice since the day before yesterday when she was telling the butcher in Fuller's how much ham to carve. The woman smiles and walks briskly on.

Secret Street was built in the 1890s for well-to-do brokers, landowners, and bankers. The houses were big enough to accommodate a servant or housemaid, with basement floors for large kitchens, and attics for staff bedrooms. As time passed, with Royal Tunbridge Wells just a forty-five-minute train ride to London Bridge, house prices in Secret Street began to creep, then bounce up, and some were bought by developers and converted into flats. In an English class-conscious way, the locals know that the top of the hill with the low numbers is the posh end, and the bottom end the flats; some bought by the council and leased to housing associations.

Towards the middle, No. 37 has been converted into an addiction rehab unit. When the planning application was displayed on the handsome lamp post outside, it caused an outcry from the good people of Royal Tunbridge Wells, whether they lived in Secret Street or not. The addicts would 'bring the area into disrepute', they said, or 'create a drug-related crime wave', or – heaven forbid – 'reduce property values'. Councillor Eustace Petty organised a petition against it, and had himself photographed by the *Tunbridge Wells Herald* on the front steps of the building, scowling, and brandishing an empty Bell's whisky bottle. Araminta risked upsetting neighbours and refused to sign the petition. She believed people with addictions need to be rehabilitated somewhere, and anyway, surely the point was that they wouldn't be drunk or taking drugs while they were there, so she couldn't see how they would need to steal to fund their habits, nor why drug dealers would waste their time hanging around on the off chance of a sale. The planning application was allowed, and the rehab unit opened, although there was no ribbon-cutting by the Mayor.

Araminta walks up to the top of the hill to No.1, a smart end terrace with a newly-painted front door flanked by large stone urns. She digs into her bag, pulls out a letter, and posts it through the door. She's planning to put a letter through every door, starting at the top of the hill and working down the odd numbers, then to cross the road to the pub at the bottom, and work her way up the evens and back home. She tends to know the neighbours in the immediate vicinity best, from taking in parcels for each other, or making small talk as they come and go, and those further down the hill, from when they walk their dogs up

the street towards the park and back again. At No. 19 –
Fran and Olivia's – the letterbox is on a spring that makes
it snatch the envelope as if it were the jaws of an
angry pit bull, and break one of Araminta's pearly-
pink painted fingernails. With a pronounced West
Country burr, she involuntarily exclaims, 'Bugger!', then
hopes no one's heard. In the corner of her eye she thinks
she sees the curtains twitch, although she's inspecting her
broken nail at that moment and can't be sure.

As Araminta approaches the rehab house, she sees
Councillor Petty outside. He's wearing his white Panama
hat over his combover which – atop his diminutive figure,
complete with short, skinny legs and pointy shoes – gives
him the impression of being a human-sized drawing pin.
Under her breath, she says, 'Bugger!' again; there's no way
she can avoid the wretched little man. Why on earth is he
up and out so early? Although she hears Fred's voice in the
back of her mind telling her not to make a scene, Araminta
steels herself to confront Councillor Petty as he stuffs a
wad of his election leaflets through the rehab door. She
musters her poshest voice,

'Hwhat in God's name are you doing? Hwhy on earth
would anyone in there vote for you?'

Councillor Petty bows his head slightly so his eyes are
just below the wide brim of his hat, and out of Araminta's
gaze.

'I'm sure everyone will want to vote for the Community
Party ...*the party that works for you*', he says, quoting the
slogan on his leaflet.

Araminta narrows her eyes and glares at him as he
scurries on to the next house. Mercifully, he's working his
way up the hill, not down. She goes to put six letters

through the door, then checks herself. The recovering addicts don't know her, and the letters are likely to end up in the bin unless they realise that she genuinely wants them there at the street party; an accepted part of the community. Better to pop round another time when they'll be up, and invite them personally. She walks to the next house, thinking how Her Majesty's penchant for two-and-three-quarter-inch heels makes for an uncomfortable walk down, but a much better walk upwards. They're finished with a lovely brass buckle, just like Her Majesty's, but bought in Hooper's department store in Mount Pleasant, not handmade by Rayne of London. Fred had flinched at the price, but Araminta had argued that you can't put a price on quality, and they look just right with her cream tweed suit. 93A is dear old Ian's flat. He's eighty, and goes everywhere on his bicycle, still working as a gardener, as he has done all his life. Always pruning, weeding, and smiling, there's something angelic about him. When it snowed last December, she met him walking to the allotments '...to see the animal prints – rabbit and fox prints', he said.

95A has a child's red bicycle left outside that's faded from red to pink in the sun, rust blooming on its brakes and chain. Seeing it makes Araminta feel suddenly breathless and queasy. She stands still for a moment and breathes deeply in through her nose and out through her mouth a few times to calm herself, then posts her letters, and hurries on down the hill.

The next and last building is the pub: The Otter Inn. Previously the Rose & Crown, the new landlord, Stephen, chose the name and transformed it from an old men's watering hole into a smart eatery and bar, with freshly painted buttermilk-coloured rendering, patio with new teak outdoor tables and chairs, and sizeable racing green parasols. Araminta thinks it a huge improvement on the old grey dump it had been before, although, the old place had lavender bushes that smelled heavenly on a summer's evening, and it was such a shame, and rather odd, that the first thing Stephen had done when he arrived was to rip them all out.

***

The other side of No. 40's front door, Ben bends down and fishes up the two pieces of post that have just landed on the doormat. He calls out to his girlfriend, Chrissy, 'The Community Party election leaflet...'

'Oh, they're good, aren't they? That councillor with the hat, whatsisname? He's good; really cares about local issues...'

'Petty, Councillor Petty... and a letter in a posh envelope. Hang on, I'll let you open it; I've just put the bins out and my hands are a bit grubby.' Ben takes the post to the kitchen where Chrissy's loading the dishwasher. She peels off her yellow Marigolds, and takes the envelope from him.

'Oh, it's really thick paper – look at this little gold crown embossed on it! Must have cost a fortune to have it printed.' Chrissy takes a knife from the kitchen drawer, and carefully opens the envelope. 'Oh gawd, it's from Mrs Hhwhat Hhwhy; silly cow!'

'Don't be mean, she doesn't do no one no harm.'

'But, honestly, old Minty Cavendish, pretending she's posh like that! Fools no one.'

'I hadn't noticed. Does she?'

'What?'

'Pretend?'

'Well, yes, obvs. What's with the stupid unnecessary "h"s?'

'She's not as posh as Beatrice at No. 2.'

'Hmm, well I suppose Beatrice *is* a bit...'

'Well, not posh exactly; she sounds like a satnav.'

'Her son's something in television.'

'What does the letter say?'

'It's about a Platinum Jubilee street party. In Secret Street. On the bank holiday in June.'

'Oh, please, no!' Ben shakes his head and grimaces. 'I've spent enough time at Her Majesty's pleasure.'

'Don't be such a misery', says Chrissy, laughing. 'It'll be fun. And look, it says here we can all join in with the preparations. We could make sandwiches, or bunting, or something. What d'you think?'

'The Royals have never done nothing for me, why should I want to celebrate that?'

'You're such a...'

Ben saunters off to the bathroom, grinning. Chrissy calls out behind him,

'It's for the community. And I *like* bunting!'

***

That evening, the proud tick of the grandfather clock in the hallway, which Araminta used to love, now sounds far too loud. She heaves the silence away by humming a little tune as she flumps up the stairs in her sheepskin slippers. After brushing her teeth, she goes to her bedroom, and as she walks in, briefly strokes the wallpaper with her fingertips. Fred had put it up; Eternal Beau, a repeating pattern of silky-looking bows with trailing ends intertwined with dainty pink buds and delicate green leaves. As a surprise for her, he'd taken the day off work to do it. She'd returned home to find he'd hung it upside down, with the trailing ribbons flailing upwards, defying gravity. When she brought herself to break it to him, he was so deflated that she couldn't be cross. In fact, his blunder had endeared him to her all the more, and the wallpaper remained just as it was.

Araminta sits at her oak dressing table, removes her hair pins, and inspects her hair for grey roots. She takes her satinwood hairbrush, stands up and walks to the sash window, where she slowly brushes as she looks out at the back garden. In the moonlight she sees a fox lope past the gazebo at the back of the lawn. It stops, as if sensing her, and looks up towards her window, but she can't be sure whether it's caught her gaze or not. Then it turns away. Its sleek, but motheaten form swerves around the chestnut tree, dips into a hollow beneath the lap wood fence, and out of sight.

Araminta returns the hairbrush to her dressing table, takes off her suit and blouse, and hangs them on wooden hangers in her wardrobe with the neatly arranged rows of skirts and jackets in cream, grey, and camel, and shelves of folded crisp white poplin blouses. She takes her long, white cotton broderie anglaise nightdress from the pillows on the double bed, and puts it on. She walks around the end of the bed, picks up Fred's freshly laundered red tartan pyjamas from his pillow, and hugs them to her heart. She takes them to Fred's wardrobe, opening the door to emptiness. For a moment, she allows herself to drink in the loss. She gently places the folded pyjamas on one of the shelves, closes the wardrobe door, walks back to her side of the bed, takes off her slippers, and gets in. She pulls the embroidered patchwork eiderdown up under her chin, reaches out for her bedside light switch, presses it, and the room turns dark with a click.

The Gene

2 Secret Street –
Beatrice's Story

Twenty years ago

Beatrice puts her silver Mercedes in first gear and indicates ready to pull out of her parking space. Hugo's girlfriend – auburn-haired, doe-eyed Scarlett – is in the passenger seat with their golden Labrador between her knees. Beatrice's mobile trills, and it's a gruff voice from Bilsden Police Station telling her that her sixteen-year-old son is being "held". As she tells Scarlett, Beatrice can almost hear the shock wave of Scarlett's eyes widening. Then Scarlett tries to look concerned and grown-up instead of excited. Now Beatrice is bundling a bewildered Fido back into the house. Little shoots are emerging from a dark place in her mind, sprouting and opening into slate grey nettles. One for how she's failed her beautiful son. Another for never dragging him out of his bedroom and sitting him down to ask how he is. Another for letting him sit in front of the television with his evening dinner, instead of around

14

the table, like a boy in a proper family in a Bisto advert. And why, of all places, did they have to take him to Bilsden? It's an abysmal, flimsy town with a pointless one-way system encircling an absurd purple bus station that looks as if it's made of plastic. The off licence has barbed wire around the roof and they serve you through a metal grille.

Approaching the police station, it looks surprisingly grand, with a Georgian façade and rows of glaring windows laid out each side of the heavy double front doors. Beatrice is thinking, 'Now I'm a criminal's mother; I park in police station car parks'. Close up, it's a granite bulging-bricked giant toad of a place; mouth gaping, ready to swallow offenders as they walk up its flicked-out tongue-steps. They hurry up the tongue, Beatrice trying not to run; not wanting to frighten Scarlett. The doors are locked. Beatrice paws at the buzzer.

'Yes?' A surly voice crackles through the intercom.

'You have my son, Hugo Sanderson.'

'Push the door.'

A metallic click vibrates uncomfortably in their ears, and Beatrice pushes, trying to avoid the sticky brown finger marks on the door panel. Inside, there's a swathe of thick glass bricks making up the reception desk and an outsized artificial weeping fig which needs dusting, and has two cigarette butts in its pot. Sergeant Surly behind the desk says, 'She can't stay here', nodding towards Scarlett. 'How old is she?'

'Fifteen?' Beatrice offers.

'She's too young. This is no place for a young lady.'

Scarlett beams at being called a young lady, and Beatrice shivers at being informed she's in an X-rated building. Sergeant Surly indicates that they should sit down on a row of those wobbly grey plastic chairs they have in public waiting areas. They go over and sit. They don't have old copies of *Country Life* on the coffee table as they do at the doctors' surgery at home. Scarlett sits upright like a meerkat. Beatrice sits there like Meryl Streep in *The French Lieutenant's Woman* on that windswept pier, gazing out to the horizon. Except she's not wearing a cloak; she's wearing her Barbour, pockets full of Gravy Bone dog treats from the abandoned walk.

***

There are two police officers in her home. Beatrice starts fussing with, 'Sorry I haven't tidied up', and, 'Would you like a cup of tea?' PC Helpful and the Special say no, she has to be present for the search. She tries not to look at the *KEEP OUT MOTHER* sign on Hugo's door as she shows them into his bedroom. In the wardrobe, PC Helpful finds a red Tupperware with a yellow teddy sticker on it, which Hugo used to use for honey cookies from Kids' Cooking Club. He peels off the lid. It's full of what looks like bits of dried-up cow dung. All the air sucks out of Beatrice's lungs. The Special picks a piece up and sniffs it. 'It's that fake formula stuff', he says. She has no idea what he's talking about, but understands from his tone that this is a good thing. He fishes under the bed and pulls out a Durex Value Pack of ten condoms, and that's when he utters, 'At least it appears he's practising safe sex, Madam'. They're all thrilled with the relief of the laughter, and from that moment the three of them are in this together.

In the police van, going back to the station, Beatrice is in the front with them, babbling about it all being her fault, and Hugo's dad being dead, and how all the time she's tried to be both mother and father to him, and failed. The Special leans forward past PC Helpful so he has eye contact, and says, 'It's not your fault, Beatrice; my mum was a single parent and I turned out alright'. He smiles, and at that moment she thinks this is the kindest thing anyone has ever said to her. Then PC Helpful unclips his radio, which has never stopped burbling, and she wonders how he knows when to listen and when to ignore it. The radio says, 'Can you pick up a prisoner on your way in?'

'We shouldn't really do this with you here', PC Helpful says.

The prisoner is ten, maybe eleven years old. He's wearing dark blue nylon jogging bottoms, a navy and white stripy t-shirt with no coat, and it's January. His grubby white plimsolls have holes in the toes. He has tousled brown hair and a thin face like a sparrow. He's led – handcuffed – by the Special from a waiting police car to their van, smiling vaguely as if he's off to the park. Beatrice resists the urge to ask if they have special small handcuffs for children. She turns around and sees that the back of the van is a cage, and realises they must have locked Hugo in there when they arrested him at the rec. The Special gets back in with them. He's holding a small yellow plastic cutlass, as you might find in a cheap Aladdin toy set from a corner shop.

PC Helpful sees Beatrice's puzzled expression and explains, 'His dad sends him out nicking car stereos. It's for breaking in through the window seals'.

***

The interview room smells of B.O. The black recording machine seems to be a portal to a different universe. PC Helpful ushers Hugo in. Beatrice thought he'd be in handcuffs. He's in his socks. He looks young. He looks old. He looks broken. He's six foot two inches of muscle and brawn, with fair, floppy hair, and wearing those ghastly shell suit bottoms he'd made her buy so he wouldn't get beaten up.

Hugo says he got it from a man in a pub he'd never met before.

Beatrice says, 'You went up to some random chap you've never seen before and asked, "Can I buy three ounces of cannabis, please?"' She looks at PC Helpful as if to say sorry, it's his interview and she shouldn't have interrupted, but he smiles encouragingly.

Realising this is the most serious game of "Who's Going to Win the Argument?" they are ever going to play, Hugo gives in quickly. 'His name's Scott. I don't know his surname. The Nag's Head.'

PC Helpful's pleased his prisoner's admitted everything without a fight, and now he can relax, get his paperwork done, and leave his shift on time. He clicks off the tape. 'With the quantity of cannabis we found on you, you should be in court in the morning, but I'm not going to do that to your poor mother.'

***

Hugo's at the desk. They've given him back his trainers. As he does up the laces, Beatrice asks, 'What d'you want to do now?' But he hears, *I'm throwing you out because that's what happens to teenage boys arrested for drugs.* It never enters her head that he's hearing that. He says, 'I'll go back to Tunbridge Wells and live with Grandma and Grandpa'. If only she'd said, *No, I want you with me. Stay here and take that place at Waterbury Sixth Form. You're clever and you'll do well.* Instead, he goes to live in that attic room, hides himself away with his computer games; sometimes drinking so much Budweiser he'd be sick out of the Velux window. He even paints the walls a mauve-pink colour; womb colour. She should have said, *Come back home and I will love you and protect you, and you will be born again into a sparkling new life,* but instead she let him go.

For six months after that, Beatrice stayed in Cambridge. She'd moved there to be with her second partner, and found a job as a legal secretary. An ordinary little job, but her colleagues were marvellous and the days passed quickly, so even after that relationship had failed, she stayed. Hugo's life had been plagued with her constant attempts at finding someone who would love her; all the relationships wrong; all of them making Hugo's life more unstable and confusing. She felt she was useless; that Hugo was better off without her. After the initial excitement of her boyfriend being arrested, Scarlett had abruptly stopped seeing him. Above all, she was embarrassed. Back in Tunbridge Wells, Hugo went to the local tech college, picked up with friends he knew from school from before he'd left, and settled down into A levels. Beatrice visited at Christmas, and found him hunched on his bed, his head bowed.

'Do you need me?' she asked. She knew this was a tricky question for him to answer. He'd always believed he was the man about the house, and – even though she'd tried hard to discourage it – tried to keep his worries from her. One

Christmas when Hugo was about seven, she found a piece of yellow paper under his pillow, with writing in red crayon: *Deer Santa, pleese can Mummy hav sum presents this yeer.* Now, in his mauve attic room, he answered her question, saying, 'It would be nice to have someone to talk to'. She gave in her notice that day, and moved back to Tunbridge Wells, where they rented a small flat near the Pantiles while they looked for somewhere to buy. He got three A levels, went off to university, and did well – a 2:1 in film production, but graduated into an England blighted by economic depression. The only work he could find was in the kitchens and bars he'd worked in as a student. Still, he worked his way up, doing catering courses and becoming a head chef in a grand hotel. Beatrice was proud of him that he hadn't done what some of his student friends had; signing on the dole, and spending their days smoking dope in their seedy town centre bedsits. But she was uncomfortable that, by working as a chef, he was following in the footsteps of a father he'd barely known. Somehow, it seemed an ominous coincidence.

Thirty-six years ago

At first, all she could think was 'blood'. When the nurse had met them at the ward entrance – his mother, three brothers and Beatrice – she wouldn't let them into the intensive care unit before explaining that George couldn't move or talk, and there were bags draining blood away from his body. But nothing could have prepared them for the sickly smell that gripped the instinctive, primeval part of them by the throat, and made them want to run away.

When Beatrice said, 'It's me; it's Beatrice', his eyes flinched behind their closed lids.

Beatrice had met George in her early twenties. Still mixed up about what life was for and – after a childhood with unhappy, bickering parents – confused about what love was meant to be. She thought it was drama, arguments, leavings and returnings, doors slammed, yelling followed by excruciating silence. George was a chef, and she worked as a waitress to help earn her keep while at university. Her parents' income was too high for her to qualify for a student grant, and they wanted her to live as they had done; understanding the value of work, championing thrift, budgeting carefully. George was tall, fair, and handsome, with a strong, deep voice that directed the chefs as if he were a conductor and they a finely tuned orchestra. He kept morale going with jokes and catchphrases; his most memorable, 'Keep smiling', often said with some irony when someone had dropped a giant pan of chilli with a clang, or smashed a catering jar of mayonnaise. He had so much life in his blue eyes. The day their relationship began, he called her to his side and whispered, 'Here's a tenner. Go over to the offy and get me a half of Bell's, then leave it in the walk-in fridge, behind the salad stuff'. She was flattered to be chosen. She took the ten pound note, rushed out and back while no one was looking, and sneaked the bottle into the fridge, then slipped the change into the pocket of his blue and white checked chef's trousers. He winked. She felt needed.

Beatrice thought she could save George by loving him. She even asked him to marry her, thinking that somehow this would make him feel safe enough to stop drinking. After the wedding, he talked about quitting, but it was always, 'Just let me get past this big banquet we're doing', or, 'Wait till after my birthday...'. Eventually she gave up, and tried to manage things with the salary from her full-time office job at Brook Street, the employment bureau, and his sporadic earnings. Thrift soon gave way to desperation when a bottle of Bell's plus beer every day cost as much as the rent, never mind the weekly groceries. His long-term girlfriend before Beatrice had given up on their relationship because there was never any money. Love was no use if you were starving and threatened with eviction. The previous girlfriend and George had been junkies together in Liverpool, but moved away to escape the heroin scene. It had worked, but then George's drinking started to take over whatever itch it was he needed to scratch, as if the only way he could exist was to be addicted to something. He used to say he'd be dead before he was thirty. Maybe it was a cry for help, but he said it as if he was almost proud of it. Was he a prophet? Or was he a fool?

George and Beatrice moved house so that George wouldn't be walking past pubs on his way home at the end of each shift. Then they discovered that the corner shop next door sold alcohol. He went in twice a day to buy a half bottle of Smirnoff. The addict's mind tells him that if he's only buying half bottles, he's drinking half as much. He was on vodka by now, because you couldn't smell it on his breath, so it was less likely people would notice. He still got too drunk and messed up, though. He was sacked on average every three to four months, but always found a new job easily. He had that private school air of confidence, looked strong, and came over as competent. He was. But he was also an addict.

As time went on, George's behaviour deteriorated. He was never violent to Beatrice, but he smashed up doors in the house, and mugs and plates often copped it. He stole anything she owned that was worth a few quid down the pub: her Pentax camera; a pair of jet earrings; a filigree silver crucifix her mother had given her; a box of original vinyl picture discs she'd collected during her teens, paid for with the money from her Saturday job at Sainsbury's. She was called in to the bank to see the manager about her overdraft. George insisted on coming with her. The manager took her bank card and cut it up in front of them. As they walked home, George shouted and cursed her all the way. She walked along behind him like some sort of puppy, in tears, while passers-by crossed to the other side of the road.

One morning he wouldn't wake up. She knew, like a sleeping dog, it was best to let him lie, but they couldn't afford for him to lose yet another job. So she set her alarm clock; a red metal Mickey Mouse one, with Micky's white cartoon gloves cheerfully pointing to the numbers, and an old-fashioned, *brring!* When it woke him, he threw it across the room and smashed it, then shouted at her for waking him. In a drunken paranoia, he said she'd let him sleep because she wanted him home with her, and didn't want him to go to work. It made no sense. She fled, and he followed her, lurching down the stairs. But then the reason for her fear altered as he stopped, his knees buckling so that he collapsed down onto the last few stairs, and sobbed. His hair flopping down over his tear-soaked face, he told her he was frightened. He couldn't trust himself with anything; even kept his cash in his socks so he wouldn't lose it. He was scared of himself every day.

Beatrice talked George into going to the GP. He had a liver function blood test. The GP told him if he didn't stop drinking he'd be dead in four years. He was twenty-six. He agreed to be booked into a detox programme run at the local hospital. Unable to afford to run a car any more, Beatrice took the bus after work to visit him each evening.

'It's pink elephants all round', he said. In typical George form, he tried to make a joke of it all, including the hallucinations. But he also said the group therapy was a waste of time, and that he shouldn't be there. 'They all sit round in this circle and talk about their problems at home; how their parents used to abuse them and everything. But I don't have any problems. I have nothing to say.' In many ways it was true. He was from a wealthy family. He'd gone to public school, his uniform bought in Harrod's each term. But his father was a top marketing executive, flying around the world for work, and was usually absent, so George and his brothers were brought up by his lonely mother. George was somehow different from them. It was as if they had no emotions. Financially rich, but culturally poor, their conversation never went beyond polite small talk, as if the family had no soul. At school, one of George's brothers had a stutter, which left him to the mercy of bullies. George challenged one of the bullies to a fight in the gym. George won, but was expelled. His mother told Beatrice that George was a troublesome child, always getting detentions at school. 'I sent him to the Boy Scouts', she said, 'but all he learned was to swear, throw stones, and light a fag in the wind'.

George's siblings all went on to have university degrees and top jobs as scientists, or in finance in the City of London. George left school without bothering to find out whether he'd passed his O Levels. His father told him, 'You spend so much time in front of bars, you might as well be standing the other side and earning money'.

When he left the detox unit, George's friends wanted him to go to the pub with them. Beatrice pleaded with them to leave him alone, but they wanted him there; the life and soul, the party animal. They said it was OK, he could drink Kaliber; an insipid alcohol-free beer that had recently been released on the market, and advertised on television by Billy Connolly. He drank one pint of it, shook his head, and said, 'Let's have a proper beer now, eh?' His friends all laughed. Beatrice died inside.

The next week she discovered she was pregnant.

Seven months later when she went into labour, George came with her in the taxi. He collapsed, drunk in the lift on the way up to the maternity ward. He'd forgotten to bring her bag, and instead brought a shopper with a bottle opener in it, just in case. The midwife found it and laughed, 'He thinks we can get the baby out with this!'

When Hugo was born, and she first looked into his dark blue eyes, Beatrice couldn't believe the love she felt for him. How could she love someone so much when she'd never seen them before? He had a birth mark on his leg, exactly the same as George's. When she saw that, an image of Hugo's name on a gravestone cut into her mind.

Maternity pay dwindling, Beatrice found a childminder so she could return to her office job and start earning again as soon as possible. But however much she earned, it was still never enough for the rent, beer money, and Smirnoff every day. Then one day, George decided to help with the decorating. It didn't go well, and soon he began that drunken roaring like an angry bear, and paint brushes started flying. Beatrice grabbed Hugo and ran into the garden.

Then Beatrice saw herself. It was as if she'd left her body and floated up above the garden where she was looking down on a young woman, trembling, cradling a baby in her arms. She thought, 'What am I doing? Why am I still with this man?' When it was just George and her, it had never entered her head to leave him, but now, with a baby, things were different. She had a responsibility to protect this fragile creature that was flinching and jolting his chubby little arms as his father crashed and bellowed. Hugo and Beatrice had to leave.

A year later, and here she was with George's carcass: a sort of bled-out George, hovering between life and death. She felt it when he left his body. 'He's gone', she whispered. His mother glared at her, but the nurse said quietly, 'I'm so sorry, George has passed away; it's only the machine that's making his lungs work'. Beatrice will never forget his mother's howl – a kind of animal sound, which ended with a shriek – 'No!' At the funeral, having left him a year before, she wondered whether his family would shun her, but George's mother beckoned her to come and sit with them up at the front of the chapel, facing the coffin. George had always said he wanted a barrel of beer by his coffin, and for everyone to have a pint and toast him. But how could they?

Still somehow the life and soul at his funeral, George's mother was amazed at all the people that came. Friends from the pub, chefs, the postman, old school friends, and lecturers from Canterbury Christ Church College. As they lowered him down, Beatrice was one of three young women in tears, in black, looking on. His ex had come, and the woman – another addict – he'd got together with after Beatrice left. His best friend gave a speech. It ended with George's catchphrase: 'Keep smiling'. Nobody did.

George's family paid for the tombstone. A small, neat, black marble thing that didn't seem to Beatrice to bear any relation to his character, apart from the inscription, which echoed his prophesy: *Here lies George Sanderson, died 20th August 1993, aged 29.*

Four years ago

'Mum, I'm in trouble.' The voice on the end of the line is Hugo's; the deep, assured voice of a thirty-two-year-old, but the words a child's. 'I need help, Mum. I need you to come and get my bank cards from me.'

She wasn't expecting cocaine. Cannabis, maybe, but not the hard stuff. She's on the platform, heart pounding in time to the chunter of the train pulling into the station. Now she's jostling through the crowd, trying to find the right platform for the connecting train, running where there's room to, making it to the train she needs just as the doors slam shut. The guard's blowing his whistle and frowning at her, 'You're too late, luv'. As the train pulls out, she feels like a mother duck whose ducklings are caught on the other side of a motorway.

She's finally made it to Snettlesham, and Hugo's waiting on the platform. She runs to hug her grown-up baby. He towers a whole foot above her, and with his solid build and that floppy fair hair, he looks, at this moment, exactly as his father did when he collapsed at the foot of the stairs in tears.

The AA rosette restaurant where Hugo earns over £70,000 a year as a head chef belongs to a grand country house hotel where the price of a room is eye-watering, and celebrities and footballers fly in by helicopter. But cocaine is snorted in the hotel bedrooms, in the plush toilets next to dispensers filled with Fortnum & Mason's hand soap, surreptitiously on the stainless steel work surfaces in the hectic kitchens.

'I swerved it, Mum, for ages...'

She wants him to cry, to let it all out, but that's not Hugo's style. 'I got on with stirring and chopping, shouting to the sous chefs, working every hour God sends to save up to buy a house with Lucy. Then she changed her mind about buying a house with me, and I just thought, 'Fuck it! What's the point?' Anyway, it made the shifts whizz by', he chuckled, trying to lighten the conversation. 'But now my savings are gone, and I've maxed out the overdraft.'

He logged in to his online bank account and sat silently, head bowed as Beatrice read, as if he were a child showing her a less-than-glowing school report. There had been a loan, then a consolidation loan. Next, it was payday loans. When the cashpoint said *INSUFFICIENT FUNDS*, he could obtain cash from Mr Lender, Money Boat, Little Loan, Speedy Cash, Cash Float, Quick Cash... In a matter of months, he'd blown his deposit for a house, and instead, owed over £15,000. 'I don't want my bank cards, Mum. Please take them, cut them up, throw them away, whatever. As long as I never have thirty quid and can just tell the dealers, "No cash, mate; no spondula...", they'll leave me alone.' Now she's in his kitchen, finding scissors in the drawer, and cutting up a purple cash card, a turquoise one, a red one, and stuffing the pieces down in the bottom of her handbag. 'Hugo', she calls, 'log in to your emails and block the payday loan companies'. She walks back into his living room, and he's already clicking through emails and blocking the senders.

Hugo, need a little extra till payday?
Exclusive offer!
Low, low interest if you borrow today!
Cash is just a click away!

Now he's gone to the kitchen to make coffees, and she's logging on to the British Association for Counselling and Psychotherapy website. Their search facility suggests a therapist who holds sessions nearby and has a degree in addiction counselling. In his website photo he looks confident and kind. Promising. The hardest thing will be telling Lucy. She comes from a nice family; one where people don't have problems with addiction or debt.

'Will you help me look for a flat, Mum? When Lucy's dad finds out, he'll come and throw me out.'

April – two months before the Platinum Jubilee street party

The church bells ring out as if they know. Beatrice is on the steps outside the big old oak doors, smiling for the family photo, wishing her mascara had been more waterproof as she licks salty tears from her mouth that's aching from smiling. She turns to accept a little hug from Lucy's mother. They coordinated in silver and blue lace mother-of-the-bride dresses, and hats with outrageously wide and celebratory brims. Lucy's father's trying to look happy, but not soppy, for the photographer, who's arranging him next to Hugo, and the bridesmaids next to

Lucy, who – but for the wings – looks like an angel in white silk. Hugo looks how she imagines George would have looked at this age, and she can't help thinking that Hugo simply still being alive would be enough for her, let alone the new job as a trainee TV production assistant, the deposit on the first house purchase, then the announcement that he and Lucy were engaged.

Soon, the white Rolls Royce limousines will take them to the reception. There will be no talk of children; Hugo and Lucy insist they don't want them. The decision is final. Bridge burnt. That addictive gene killed Hugo's father and nearly ruined Hugo's life, too. She reluctantly agrees with them. If Hugo made her a grandmother, she'd be watching the child with him, looking for that birth mark, seeing visions of gravestones, watching its teenage reaction to alcohol, maybe cannabis, cocaine. An addict is always an addict, whether recovered or not. In the backs of their minds, Lucy and Beatrice will always worry about Hugo and whether he'll ride the next wave of temptation, or drown in it.

Beatrice never knew whether George loved her. She knows how ridiculous that sounds; he married her, apart from anything else. But whichever way you look at it, alcohol was more important to him than she was, and it was more important to him than his son. That's not apportioning blame; it's simply stating a fact. If addiction can be stronger than love, then maybe the only way for love to win is for that rascal, that rapscallion gene to be stopped. Just as the multicoloured confetti they're throwing now will be captured in the wedding album family photo – forever suspended in the air around them.

The Date

'It's time you stopped moping over Dad. I doubt he thinks of you at all', says Becky's voice, slightly crackly from Araminta's mobile.

'Hang on love', replies Araminta, 'I'll take you upstairs'. The mobile signal in Secret Street tends to be a bit iffy. The phone company, 5G, had put in a planning application for a phone mast in St. John's Road, but the locals had been outraged and created a petition against it. Araminta's daughter continues talking as Araminta climbs the stairs to the back bedroom, which used to be Becky's, and now has a double bed, so Becky can come and stay with her husband when they visit. Becky continues, 'He only thought of himself'.

'Fred... your father, had his reasons.' Araminta always felt it was her fault; the whole thing had been her fault. She walks to the left one of the two fitted wardrobes, opens it, and stares at the empty shelves; the hanging rail with a single wooden coat hanger soundlessly swinging. One day she'll stop thinking of it as his, and put in some of her own clothes. But not yet.

'Yes, cock-related reasons.'

'Oh, Becky, really...'

'It's true, Mum. So, come on, I've been telling you to get on that dating app for years. You said you would.'

'It seems completely ridiculous at my age.'

'What's ridiculous about love?' asks Becky, and her mother thinks she can't really argue with that.

'Anyway', Araminta continues, 'I've lost the link'.

'I'll send it to you again. And register on it this time, OK?'

Araminta would have felt bullied if she hadn't been so completely sure that Becky loved her. They'd rarely fallen out, even when Becky had teenage strops and unsuitable boyfriends. Then, when all the trouble had started, Becky had been a source of strength. Jenny, the younger one, had taken her father's side, as if they'd subconsciously chosen their roles out of fairness, so the parents had one child each to support them.

'Jenny would not approve. At all', says Araminta.

'Stuff Jen! And she's in Australia, anyway, so she can sit there on her high horse, upside down, and disapprove all she likes.'

'Really, though, darling, I'm eighty-two...'

'You still do your Jane Fonda, don't you?'

'Well, yes, but not in a leotard and sweatband.'

Becky giggles. 'Anyway, you know it'll go well, as long as you remember to take...'

'What? Take what?' says Araminta.

'You *must* remember what you used to say to Jen and me when we were little', says Becky. '"With your Rain-mate..."'

'Oh! Yes', says Araminta, '"...your Handy Andies, and..."'

'"A pocketful of love"', they chorus, '"you're ready for anything."'

Araminta laughs. 'I'm not sure a plastic rain bonnet and a tissue will save me from a serial killer.'

'He won't be a serial killer, Mum, don't be silly. Right, I'm sending the app now!'

Araminta's mobile plinks.

'Do it! OK? I'm ringing off now, and you do it right away! Go on, go on, go on...' The call goes dead. Araminta laughs, shakes her head, and sits down on the bed.

The app has a rather garish fuchsia pink logo, which she clicks as if she were touching a mouse a cat had brought in. It asks if she's a man or a woman, and if she's looking for a woman or a man. At least she knows the answer to that. She chooses *woman looking for man*. Then it asks for her email address, and she has to tick the terms and conditions box. If she reads all that, she'll never go through with it, so she ticks and presses *Sign me up!* She has to confirm her marital status. She wants to tick the box for *widow;* that's what everyone believes she is, but she thinks if she's going to do this, she should do it properly, so she clicks *divorced*.

The app asks for her level of education, which surprises her, but she supposes it makes sense, especially after all the effort she's made to improve herself. It asks how important her partner's level of education and intelligence is, and she has no idea how to answer. Becky's husband is famously quite dim, yet a lovelier man you couldn't hope to find, and he's great with their children. She ticks *unimportant*, then has to specify her height, and how important it is that her partner is as tall as her. She thinks of Jerry Hall and Rupert Murdoch, and decides it shouldn't be important at all, but is, and clicks the box for *over 5'9"*. She isn't bothered about ethnicity. It asks if she's satisfied with her appearance, and she ticks, *mostly*, then that it's *slightly important* that her partner has an attractive appearance, wondering how on earth the app is going to judge anyway.

The tricky question is, *Which role would you like a partner to fulfil the most?* She's getting on a bit for *husband or wife*. *Someone to enjoy life with* makes sense. *Dreamy lover*, it suggests. Hmm... at their age it's more about can he afford Viagra and put up with KY jelly. Not very romantic. *Partner to adventure with*. That's a nice idea. *My closest confidant*. That's somehow nicer still. She picks the last.

She laughs aloud at the skydiving picture on, *What activity are you most likely to choose for a first date?* The other three pictures seem to be suggesting a candlelit dinner, a concert, or a trip to the cinema. She can't imagine falling in love at the Odeon, so picks the concert and the candlelit dinner, although, eating in front of someone isn't terribly romantic, not if you have sauce dribbling down your chin. The app goes on to ask her characteristics: *good conversation skills; politeness; spontaneity...* Lord knows she wants to be more spontaneous, so she chooses that one. Then there's a blur of questions about *first kiss*, *desire for sex* (how would she know until she met him?) and *meeting his friends*, which, remembering Fred's friends at the golf club, puts her off a bit. It asks what's important in a relationship. She wants so badly to click *honesty*, but the thought of it fazes her. How can she be honest after all this time and tell someone about her roots; who she really is? But she's almost at the end of all the questions now, and curious to see if there are actually any single men in the area looking for an eighty-two-year-old partner. She doesn't have to meet any of them. In fact, she can have a look, then delete the app if she wants to. Next are questions about whether she's *protective*, or *patient*, or *understanding...* She has no idea, and ticks *slightly applies* to the lot of them. She picks *spontaneous*, *caring*, and *warm* as her important attributes in a partner, not sure that she's choosing the right categories at all.

It asks her name. She writes *Araminta*. She thinks of the honesty category, and goes to change it, but then leaves it as *Araminta*. For *year of birth*, she seems to have to scroll forever until she reaches *1941*. Then she puts in her profession as, *retired teacher*, and it asks her income level. 'How impertinent!' she says out loud, then laughs. Her teacher's pension isn't that brilliant, but with her state pension she just creeps up into the second category.

'With your Rain-mate, your Handy Andies, and a pocketful of love, you're ready for anything', she thinks, and presses the final box: *FIND MY MATCH!*

Pages of men stare out at her from little boxes; a sea of grey-haired hopefuls. Bob is plumped up on pillows with a pained expression, as if on his deathbed. Afzal has written, *Not a lot to say, but happy and sappy*. What does that even mean? Patrick has a photograph of himself bare-chested. Uggh! Considering his age (seventy-seven) the photo has clearly been taken years ago, in fact, going by the mullet, probably some time in the eighties. Alan looks as if he's about to be interrogated by the police, and Jack looks far too pleased with himself. Mark, *3 x widowed*, doesn't sound safe to be around. Brian's nose fills the entire screen. Poor Brian. Someone called André states he's been *single my whole life*, and looks suspiciously like Robert Plant. And someone called Darren, who's missed all of his face out apart from his forehead when uploading his selfie. Darren is clearly useless. Douglas looks as if he's just been dug up. This is hopeless.

She feels a little guilty, as these are all real people, and she's behaving like a child in a sweet shop, casting them aside as if they were the Parma Violets nobody likes.

After much mulling, Araminta decides that she likes the look of Bill. He's wearing a white dress shirt, dickie bow and dinner jacket, in a photo clearly taken by a friend or relation at some sort of event, rather than professionally. He looks extremely likeable, with a smile that seems genuine; almost cheeky, but not too cheeky. Actually, the more she looks at his face, the more she surprises herself, thinking it's a face she could fall in love with. What a silly old woman she's becoming. She clicks on his profile. *Plumber* it says, and that he's bought his own council house in Sherwood. She's disappointed. Lovely as he is, Bill the plumber simply won't do for Araminta Cavendish. Below Bill's profile picture is a spectacularly good-looking man, with the bluest eyes she's ever seen; Tony. He's seventy-nine, a retired solicitor, and widowed. Perfect.

***

It had taken Araminta three days to pluck up the courage to contact Tony, but she was relieved to find he was eloquent, thoughtful, and polite. He talked to her online about his retirement, how he'd been on two cruises on his own, and – although he'd enjoyed them – he would have enjoyed them so much more with a beautiful lady like her to share them with. Araminta soaked up the flattery. She'd used a recent profile photo from when she last visited Becky in Berwick-upon-Tweed. She'd been in a pleasure boat, pointing out two leaping dolphins, and the excitement of seeing them had lit up her face and made her look vibrantly alive. Tony was keen to meet. In fact, yesterday evening, he'd talked her into meeting for coffee this morning. She'd ticked the box for *spontaneous*, so she agreed. He said that he would carry a rolled-up copy of *The Times*, and she thought that was a sweet little joke.

It had seemed deliciously exciting last night, but this morning, walking up the stairs to meet Tony in Hooper's restaurant, everything about the date feels wrong. For a start, she'd inconveniently dreamed of Bill last night, which left her feeling confused when she woke up. She'd had to tweeze out a whisker from her chin that had appeared overnight, which was not, thought Araminta, what a woman should be doing when seeking romance. She's wearing a camel-coloured dress, which suits her complexion, but makes her look ancient. She's had to take her shoe off twice on the way to Hooper's to try and shake out a tiny stone, but has been unable to find it, and is now walking with a slight limp. She's forgotten to put a pack of Handy Andies in her bag, and has a sniffle from the cool, damp spring air. She wants to turn back, return to her car, and drive home to sit with her feet up on the sofa, a good book, a shortbread, and a pot of freshly ground coffee. But it would be cruel to stand Tony up.

Araminta's a little early. The restaurant is surprisingly empty for a Saturday morning. It's decorated with sage green walls, comfortable padded cream leatherette chairs and warm pine tables, but today the sage green seems a little suffocating. The woman behind the counter is friendly, and they chat about the new avocado and carrot cake with its startling, almost fluorescent, green buttercream icing. Maybe she'll take a risk and order a slice when Tony arrives. She orders an Americano and chooses a table near the doorway in case she needs to make a quick getaway. Three tables are taken. One with two women around her age, with hair in identical grey bobs, chatting about something they're looking at on an iPad. At another sits a lone woman doing a crossword. She has grey hair in a French pleat, like Araminta's. The third has another single, older woman, but... no, a man, presumably her husband, is walking towards her with a tray holding two coffees. Araminta checks her watch. It's 10.55, so she's still five minutes early. She stares at the pink smudge her Elizabeth Arden lipstick has left on her cup, then looks out of the window at Britten's music shop. There's a 'cello in the window. Such a beautiful shape, in spruce and maple that almost glows. It looks as if it's waiting for someone to take it home and play it. In the corner of her eye, Araminta sees someone's coming in; a man. A man with a white Panama hat and a beaky nose.

Councillor Petty. Of all people! For a moment, Araminta panics that he could be her date, but mercifully he has no rolled up copy of *The Times*. Still, she doesn't want him to know why she's there. She tries to picture a way of allowing Tony to approach her for the first time in real life without it looking to Councillor Petty like a blind date. If she says something like, 'How lovely to see you again', Tony will think her odd. This whole thing is going to be a disaster. At least Councillor Petty's ignoring her, which saves her the trouble of ignoring him. Sneaking glances at him to make sure he doesn't notice, she watches him order a coffee and a piece of flapjack, and take it to a table where he sits alone and stares blankly out of the window at the station. It occurs to Araminta that he might be lonely, just like her, and that – if you think about it objectively – she's just as much of a fraud as he is. But she brushes her sympathetic stirrings away; she isn't finished with loathing him, yet.

On the dot of 11.00, in walks a man in his late seventies with a handsome face, but wearing ankle-swinger-length two-tone denim jeans, mid-blue at the front, and bleached at the back. Beneath them, white socks with black trainers. In his hand, a rolled-up copy of *The Times*. He scans the room, hoping for one of the women to identify themselves. It doesn't matter to Araminta how stunningly gorgeous his face is, she could never, ever, be seen dead with a man wearing two-tone jeans and white socks. White socks! She shudders. Hopefully she looks sufficiently different to her profile photo that he can't be sure it's her. She stands up, abandons her coffee, flees through the coffee shop entrance, through the racks resplendent with lace and silk in the lingerie department, and towards the stairs. For a moment, she's afraid he'll come after her, but he doesn't.

She hurries down the stairs to the ground floor beauty section, past the young shop assistants with their glowing complexions and glossy hair, past the designer shoes with heels of a height she's long since given up wearing. Becky meant well, but she really shouldn't have listened to her. Dating at her age makes as much sense as her buying the flimsy purple lace G-string that had just caught her eye in Lingerie upstairs. Those days are gone.

She thinks of the two grey-haired women in the café, amiably chatting over an iPad. She doesn't need a man; she needs friends. How can she be eighty-two and have no friends? It's embarrassing. How has this happened? She can think of friends she's had in the past, but then, were they really friends, or were they actually just colleagues? Apart from Christmas and birthday cards, she hasn't kept in touch with anyone much since she retired. She speaks to some of the neighbours of course. But is a neighbour a friend? Not really. What she needs to do is turn those relationships into friendships. But how? You can't just walk up to someone and ask them to be your friend. Maybe when you're eight, but not when you're eighty-two.

40 Secret Street – Ben

The next day

Araminta turns the key in her Mini Cooper's ignition again. Instead of the engine roaring into life, there's a pathetic little click. She wants to pop to Waitrose. It's a twenty-minute drive and the traffic won't be much fun on a Saturday morning, but – incomprehensibly – there's no Waitrose in Tunbridge Wells, she's run out of leaf tea, and needs must. She shuffles in her glove box for her RAC letter. Her membership expired three months ago. What to do? She would never usually ask for help, but she remembers she's now on a mission to make friends. The answer's obvious: Ben. Ben, at No. 40, is the Secret Street go-to neighbour if you need anything in an emergency. He'd fetched a ladder and helped Nancy get into her house through an open upstairs window when she'd locked herself out, and fixed the boiler for Arthur and Denise when it had stopped working and they didn't have a clue what to do.

Ten minutes later and Ben's opening her bonnet and looking at the battery. As he bends awkwardly over her car,

Araminta realises how tall he is. Ben must be well over six foot, with a mop of curly red hair above a smile that seems incongruously sweet on such a scarred face.

'Definitely the battery. How long you had it?'

'Oh, I don't really know, at least, um...'

'They tend not to last more than five years.'

'More than that, I think.'

'I can take you to Halfords on the industrial estate to get one if you like?'

Accepting help like this makes her feel like a cliché of a lonely old woman, and vulnerable. 'I couldn't possibly trouble you', she says.

Ben smiles and says, 'Nah, come on, it's OK, I'm not working today'.

Even though her stomach churns, she hears herself say, 'Well, it's really very good of you indeed'. She walks with Ben down the hill to his house on the bend, where his battered blue Ford Focus is parked outside.

'What do you do? For work?' she asks, then immediately worries she's being too nosy.

Ben doesn't seem to mind. 'Roofer', he says. 'That's where you'll find all the ex-cons; up on the roof.'

Ben's words ring in Araminta's ears. Is he telling her he's a criminal? It doesn't make sense that such a helpful, kind man could be an "ex-con", as he puts it. What if it's murder, or something violent? She thinks of his scars. How did he come by them? Is it polite to ask? Is she going to be safe in the car with him? Surely it couldn't be anything violent; he's such a sweet-natured man. Maybe it's just something boring, like unpaid parking tickets; something dull.

'You've gone very quiet', Ben says. They're on the Pembury Road now, in the customary Saturday morning traffic jam. 'I know what you're thinking, and I'm gonna tell you. But I'm not sure where to start.'

'Well, start at the beginning, I suppose. If you're happy to trust me with your story, I would be honoured to hear it.'

Araminta's used to people telling her their stories. She'd thought about it a lot, but had never quite been able to put her finger on why. She must just have one of those faces. Rose, for example, a newly qualified teacher Araminta barely knew, tearfully told her she'd just discovered her boyfriend had been sexually abusing his little sister. Later, Araminta asked Rose why she chose her to talk to about it. Rose replied, 'Because I knew you wouldn't bat an eyelid'. When the kids were playing up in Rose's class, Araminta wanted to explain to them that they had no idea what Rose was going through, and to be kind. But she couldn't. Sometimes her head feels heavy with untold secrets.

The traffic jam allows them to creep about ten more metres, but now Ben shifts back from first into neutral and puts the handbrake on. 'I wanna give you my story, I really do, but it's hard y'now? My childhood, you see... it was pretty shit, to be honest. My father fucked off when I was four months old. I lived with my mum and nan. Then I lost my grandad as well, when I was five.'

'So the men in your life kept disappearing?'

'Yeah, that was a massive thing for me. I don't wanna meet my father, though. He's probably dead now, anyway. I wanna see a photo; see where I come from. That bothers me, 'cause I don't know nothing, except that his name's Stewart Campbell, at the time of my birth he was a bookie's assistant, and he's a tall, red-headed Scotsman.' Ben gestures from his red hair down his long body to his feet, and laughs. 'My mum married this bloke, Jim, and we moved into his house. He was a bit strange; spent most of his time in the shed. He was a brickie. Big fella he was; big hands. Mum was having affairs with other people. When she was out, Jim would stand at the window and watch for her to come home, and if Mum come from the left she was coming home from work; if she come from the right, she'd been having an affair.' Ben chuckles again. Araminta doesn't laugh. She isn't a fan of adultery, and she's not sure whether it's funny or not. But maybe Ben isn't laughing because it's funny; perhaps he's laughing because it's too painful for him to allow himself to be sad.

'Jim had a brother, Graham. He moved into the house when I was seven, eight, maybe? I lived in the attic – hot in the summer, cold in the winter. I remember peering into Graham's bedroom, and it was dark and dirty and the walls was just black, filthy, like he's been wiping his dirty greasy hands all over them. He had a piss pot under his bed, and it stank. He looked a bit like Elvis, with jet-black hair. Although the black, it might have been dirt.' Ben chuckles. 'He used to scare me, he'd come out of his room and say horrible things, like the Bogey Man was coming to get me and strip my skin off; stuff like that. Dinner times he'd sit at the table with a vest on and an Andy Cap hat. I'd get told off for something, slapped round the face, and I'd have to eat my dinner sitting on the stairs. I'd sit there with my head bowed, so I didn't have to look at him.'

'It sounds absolutely awful.' Araminta looks at Ben's profile next to her in the car and thinks at that moment he looks like a child.

'Once my mum flipped out and broke every window in the house. We got taken out of the house by the police, but then we had to go back and live there, with every window boarded up.

'Eventually, when I was about fifteen, Mum met a bloke who lived in Margate. She just left; went to live with him and left me at the house. I didn't speak to her for a year after that.'

'So you stayed in the house with Graham and your stepdad, Jim?'

'Yeah. Jim used to lock all the food in his bedroom, so I thought, "Fucking hell, I'm not paying you rent no more." I remember once all there was in the cupboard was this can of oxtail soup. I detest oxtail soup! I put everything I could find – salt, pepper, sugar, brown sauce, ketchup, anything – trying to make it edible. It wasn't edible. I must have stayed there till the age of about eighteen. I was a building site labourer at the time, so I'd come home from work covered in dust and stuff and I'd turn the immersion on and he'd turn it off again. I needed a bath; I was filthy! And I'd come home sometimes and there'd be dead rabbits hung over the bath...'

'Sorry?'

'Yeah, dead rabbits dripping blood into the bath – blood trickling down into the plughole. So I just went up the pub. Had a roll-up there and a few pints. Used to spend my time there because I didn't wanna be home. That went on for years. That was my life. I started getting in trouble with the police from about the age of eleven; mixed with the wrong people. Silly things; fighting and things like that. Anyway, so, I'd split up with my girlfriend, lost my job. It was the recession I think; there wasn't a lot of work. Down to three-day week, two-day week... I'd just had enough. So one evening, Jim started, and I was at my limit. I didn't hit him, but threatened him. He kicked me out the house. So I had to phone up my mother. She'd sent me a letter by then, apologising, y'know, for leaving. I phoned her from the phone box and she said, "I'll come and get you", and I ended up staying with her in Margate.'

'Was that better, then?'

'Yeah. I got my own flat soon after and I loved it: my own independence, cupboard full of food...'

'No rabbits over the bath.'

'No, no rabbits over the bath.' Ben smiles, then frowns again. 'But then I kept getting in trouble with the police. I used to drink too much and end up with alcohol blackouts. I was capable of doing horrible things and not knowing about it. That carried on for a few years and I ended up in prison. Mainly fighting people. I only used to bash people that deserved it. When I was at school I was always fighting. I got handy with my fists. People say that I was obviously in with the wrong crowd, but I say, "Yeah, but I was wrong as well. They didn't make me wrong; it was my choice." Wherever I went there were idiots, and I was an idiot, too. I used to take it upon myself to help people; undo their wrongs. I don't know what it was; like a saviour or something.'

'A vigilante?'

'Maybe. So one of my ex-girlfriends – I think it was her ex – he owed her child money so I thought I'd go and get the money for her. I went round and knocked on his door. He'd took her telly and money and stuff, so I said, "I want fifty quid off you to give to the child."

'"Yeah", he said, "I'll sort that out for you." I said, "OK". Two weeks later, he still hadn't done, so I went round to his house and put his door through. I said, "I want the money."

He said, "I'll sort it out," and I said, "No, you've had two weeks to sort it out, and this is for a child." Anyway, so I bashed him up. He went round saying that me and six of my mates beat him up. So anyway, I hit his girlfriend as well – didn't mean to – she's got behind me to try and stop me, and as I'm hitting him, I pull my arm back to hit him, and I elbow her.'

Ben demonstrates pulling his elbow back, then drives a few more metres, allowing two cars waiting in a side road to drive in front of him. 'She never got the money, I don't think.' The driver now in front flashed his hazards as a thank you.

'I like it when people bother to do that', says Araminta.

'It's illegal, I think', says Ben. 'Nice, but illegal.' They're past the traffic lights and travelling at thirty again. 'Anyway, I used to enjoy a fight as a kid. I hate it now; it makes me feel sick, but when I was growing up, we used to go to different towns for a fight. We'd sit in a pub and stare at each other and a fight would kick off. I've made a lot of good friends out of people beating each other up, silly as that sounds.'

Araminta tries to imagine enjoying a fight, but can't. Ben's is a completely alien culture to hers.

'So then I went to prison the first time; twenty-one days for non-payment of fines. The fines was for fighting and stealing cars. I didn't drive, but my mate could, so I went with my mate. That was my first experience of jail. Elmley in Sheerness. I only did a week and a half. It was scary first time, but I always wanted to go to jail, to experience it.'

'Like a badge of honour, you mean?'

'No, I was just curious. If things got violent, I knew I could look after myself, but when I first went in, it was a bit daunting, really. Anyway, I done my time. Then I got sent back again for bashing up police officers; got forty-eight days for that one. I used to think it was alright to bash police because it was part of their job. I respect the police an awful lot now; I've grown up a lot. Then I went to jail again; six months for fighting... someone... some random, I can't remember why. Nothing seemed quite right about that. To this day I don't think it was me; I don't remember it. Everything was wrong; the description was wrong; almost sounded like I'd been set up. Anyway I did six months for that, and by this time I'm prison-savvy now, it didn't bother me. If anything I enjoyed it a little bit.'

'What's it like, though, when you first go in?'

'The first impression of prison is just how massive it is, 'cause it's got all the wings. Lots of people in there. You daren't look at anyone. I've met a lot of nice people in prison, but then you've also got the worst of the worst; that's why they're in there. I'm not saying that I didn't deserve to be in there. Just wanted to get in and get out. I wanted to see a prison and I'd seen it. I must have been about twenty-one when I was first in there. The first night I put my head on a pillow was a bit weird, 'cause it sort of sets in that you're in prison now. Then you wake up in the morning and your eyes don't open up into your bedroom; you're in a cell, and there's someone else in there with you. That's quite emotional; quite upsetting.'

'Lonely, but with someone else in the room?'

'I s'pose.'

They're parking outside Halfords.

Ten minutes later and they're back in Ben's car with Araminta's new battery in the boot.

Araminta asks, 'What are the cells like? Do you have...' she refrains from using the term "en suite". 'Do you have a toilet in the cell?'

Ben nods.

'So did you have to share that? Was there any privacy?'

'No, not really...'

'Was it like a little half a wall, sort of cubicle thing?'

'No, some of them are just a toilet so you have to sit there, like... it was quite hard... When I first went in, I didn't go to the loo for five days I don't think, so I had to apologise to him – my cell mate – when I first did. As you can imagine, it wasn't very pleasant. He said, "Oh you stink!" I said, "Well, I haven't been, mate, for about five days." That's nerves I think, having to defecate in front of someone. Obviously when someone's on the toilet you turn and look the other way, but there's still a person in that small, tiny room with you.'

'What about food?'

'So basically, you come back from work, then you'd get locked up for about an hour, hour and a half, then they'd come and unlock you for lunch, so you'd go round and get your roll or whatever. All prisons work on different systems. So, some prisons you get up in the morning to get your breakfast and you'd pick up your lunch at the same time, so you'd get a roll. If you don't get up, you don't get no breakfast and you don't get no lunch. So you take it and you eat it in your cell. Or you can sit in the canteen if you like, with tables. So you sit there and the screws they walk up and down the aisle.'

'What was in the rolls?'

'You get ham, cheese, or chicken... normally there's a choice. I broke my tooth in there, on a baguette... not great some of 'em!'

'Oh dear. What do the cells look like; how are they decorated?'

Araminta immediately wishes she hadn't asked; it's as if she's after the *Homes & Gardens* magazine experience. This is prison. This is Ben's life.

'The walls are usually cream – Magnolia I s'pose – eggshell. Most cells are filthy with people writing all over the walls, and you use toothpaste to stick posters up and then you've got lumps where the paint was just painted all over the toothpaste. The decorators were prisoners so they'd just come in and paint over everything.'

'Did you have posters?'

'I didn't put up posters; I did drawings.'

'Wow! So you're an artist then?'

'Piss artist!'

'What sort of thing did you...'

'Abstract... what I'd do, if there was, say, A4 paper, I'd draw dots like a centimetre apart in like an 'L' shape and then I'd put lines from the top one and come down to the bottom one, and it makes, like, a bend, and then I'd colour them in black and white. It's hard to explain. I've got some in my house if you want to come and see them.'

***

Twenty minutes later, Ben and Araminta are standing on Ben's landing, looking at his framed artwork on the wall.

'So this art would be from my last jail I was in when I done five years. That was all done in Bic biros.'

'Is that because that's all you could get hold of?'

'You could get hold of other pens, but when I was in a later jail, a fella in there said, "Why don't you paint?" I said, "I can't paint, mate!" He says, "You could do this with acrylic." Sam, his name was; lovely, lovely fella... helped me out so much. So I done these for my girlfriend, Chrissy, as a birthday present...'

The monochrome painting has a background divided in two; black on the left, and white on the right. A shape like a twisting net seems to dance from the left to the right so that each time it moves, it becomes new.

'Basically the idea of them is s'posed to be... so the light hits it one side... so you can imagine... there's a dark side...'

The next painting has a cavernous, brown background on which a geometric shape seems to hover. It's shaded to give a three-dimensional appearance, like a cut diamond, with an empty centre, in the shape of a...

'What shape is that?' Araminta asks.

'Well, it's an eye, isn't it?' Ben replies, as if it's obvious. The eye stares back at them. 'They asked me all that stuff, y'know, therapy questions, but I can't be bothered with all that. Hang on a minute...' Ben goes to one of the bedrooms and returns with a torch which he shines on the painting. The background that was brown now glows in a deep orange, and the eye glows sapphire blue.

'That's gorgeous!'

'Fluorescent pens. It was Blantyre House where I done that.'

'What was Blantyre House?'

'An open prison. It used to be the flagship of British prisons. It was a hard jail to get into, but 'cause I was a model prisoner...'

Araminta giggles, wondering whether she should. 'It sounds like choosing private school.'

'Yeah.' He smiles. 'When you're in higher category jails, then you do courses. They accepted me 'cause my record was perfect and when I was in there I was a very good boy.' Ben walks back downstairs and Araminta follows him. They sit on his brown corduroy sofa in his front room.

'Tea?' Ben asks.

'That would be lovely.'

Ben shows Araminta photos on his phone of other artworks he's created and leaves her scrolling through them while he makes the tea. Araminta can't help noticing an album on his phone with the caption, *Pain*. She doesn't want to ask, but as he returns with two steaming mugs, she can't resist. 'I can't help asking, what's this?'

'Oh, you don't wanna see that one; it's not very pretty...'

'What is it, though?' She peers at his phone.

'It's my Pain Album; all injuries; my injuries.' Ben laughs.

Araminta doesn't. In her West Country accent, she exclaims, 'Lord preserve us!' It looks like stills from a horror movie. Every picture shows a wound: a jagged cut on his head; a gash on his leg; his face bandaged with blood trickling down it; a slash down his stomach, as if it's some kind of abdominal surgery. One seems to be... what is it? It's an ear, with so much blood and swelling around it, it doesn't look real.

'I was in Sticky's, and I got smashed in the face with a glass... for no reason... it was five mill from my jugular and this was like, Christmas; the day before Christmas, and that was in the year of getting out of jail on parole. They was after some bloke for drugs. It's all caught on CCTV, and I've seen the footage of it, and the police said, "They were just

gonna hurt anyone that day and unfortunately it was you."
So, broken bottle... there, there, there, back of me neck,
fractured my eye socket... see the bruise on it? For nothing.
I said, "If I'd stood on his foot I could understand it." 'Cause
what I've done in my past to people, 'specially to my last
victim, it was kinda like, well, you deserve what you got,
really. And even the police, they said, "You don't deserve
that." Y'know, they said, "You've done your time and you've
learnt and everything."'

Before Ben had a chance to ask about her sudden change
of accent, Araminta quickly asks, 'So what happened with
your last victim? Why did he deserve it?'

'Raped my stepdaughter.'

Araminta takes a sharp intake of breath.

'Yeah. So, I'm livin' in Margate now, so, um, er... so I'm
working with my friend, plastering. So, I think I had four
cans of beer on the way home. He dropped me off the end
of the road; we'd had a laugh, 'cause it'd be me and my best
mate at the time, so yeah, he dropped me off the end of the
road, all happy and smiles and that. So I walk past the house
where the fella... they said it wasn't statutory rape 'cause
she was fourteen and he was seventeen. She had ADHD
and learning disability problems; she was vulnerable. She
would do things like nick our fags and give them to people
just to try and get friends, so, she... yeah, they basically
took advantage of her. They said it wasn't statutory; wasn't
forced upon her... well, I don't care; she was fourteen, you
know?'

'I would have thought the law was wrong there...'

'The police said the same. They said, "We would've done
the same as you, but we would've got caught." Anyway, so

I'm walking up the road and I see the boy who... raped my stepdaughter...'

'How did you know it had happened?'

'Someone come and told me.'

'How did they know?'

''Cause they was in the room when it was happening. There was these lads in the flat and one of them come and told me because he didn't agree with it. Well, I wanted to kill that rapist. I didn't; I phoned up the police, social services, 'cause she used to see child psychologists, and they was involved, but it was going nowhere... um... so he's leant out the window and he was like, "I didn't do nothing; I didn't touch her..." So I said, "Come down here and tell me that then." So he did. Which I was quite shocked about, but a little bit of respect, mate, even if you *are* stupid... I didn't do anything to him, but I said, "Stay down here, don't come up the road." (I lived in the same road and there was a park up the end.) So a week later, I come up the road again and I says to my partner, "Where's Kylie?" – that's the name of the child – and she says, "She's in the park." So I went down the park and there he is with her. So I grabbed hold of him, scruff of the neck, lifted him off the floor and threw him down the road. I said, "Fucking stay away, mate, 'cause if you don't, I'm gonna kill ya'." Left it like that, still waiting for the police to do something... um... she had one interview with the police. Apparently the other one was a bit much and she couldn't do it. Nothing seemed to be happening.

'Anyway, so this day – the day it happened – so I'm sitting on the kerb with a couple of friends at the end of my road having another couple of drinks getting a bit more pissed... um... so... lad that raped her and his friend and the rapist's dad walked up the road. So I said to the father,

"You need to keep your son away from my daughter." And I said to him what he'd done and he turned round to his son and the son said, "No, I haven't done anything." So this bloke come up to me, this far away from my face...' Ben holds his palm an inch in front of his nose, 'and said, "Next time you wanna fucking speak to my son, you come an' fucking speak to me first." Well, that was it; I suffered an alcohol blackout and it turned very, very bad for him. Three o'clock in the morning the Old Bill turned up and said, "I'm arresting you..." and that. I said, "Fair enough, gi's a minute to get dressed." They didn't handcuff me or nothing. Walked to the car. I knew what I'd done... not the severity of what I'd done to him, but that I'd covered him in blood and that, um... Took me to the police station, took me down to an interview room, interviewed by CID. They had to tell me what I'd done; I had no recollection of it. I basically knocked him to the ground, kicked him, punched him, kicked him in the head a few times. He was in hospital for six months; had reconstructive surgery to his face. There's no excuse for that; doesn't matter what the reasons are, a human being shouldn't do that to another human being...' Ben's voice trails off. He stares at the floor. Araminta instinctively knows she shouldn't interrupt. It's as if this moment of silence is in honour of his victim.

Then Ben takes a deep breath in and out. 'I was so disgusted with what I done to that man; it shook me up to know that I was capable of *that* much violence, it, it... it was horrendous. The thing is, before that, I used to start fighting and bashing people up, but I just used to knock them on the floor and that was that; never to the extreme. And half the time you'd end up in the pub with them afterwards, y'know... But that kind of, yeah... when they read it out I broke down in the interview room, it was just... I thought, I can't do this; I can't continue like this; this is just wrong. And, er... I seen people get beaten up in prison and it made me feel physically sick watching it happen. I made my mind up that was it for me; I don't wanna be this horrible person any more. I hated myself. Worst thing about it was, it wasn't him; it was the son, and all they done was move the son out of the area, change his name, and put him somewhere else, so he could have more victims.' He shakes his head and sighs. 'Finding out what I was capable of was the turning point for me. Eventually... If you knew me before, you wouldn't like me. I didn't wanna be that horrible thug – or whatever I was – any more. I didn't want people to think... Actually, I don't care about what other people think of me, *I* gave a fuck, *I* cared about me, and I didn't wanna be that person.'

'So what did you do?'

'What *could* I do? I got life.

'At first I didn't understand what was going on. I was in the court – Crown Court – pleaded guilty all the way with it, put my hands up, y'know, um... so the judge was like...' Ben makes a noise like a racing car, '...gabbling away at top speed. He mentioned "five years", so I thought that's what I'd got. In a few seconds he'd finished, and I was like, what happened there? So I turned to the usher and I said, "What happened?" And the usher said, "I don't know, it was so fast, but your barrister's downstairs..." (This was the barrister that had turned round to me and said, "I think you'll be better off if you represent yourself; it'll look better", and I says, like, "I've never been in a Crown Court in me life; haven't got a clue.")

So then I got taken down by the two security and I said to them, "I've just never experienced anything like it; the judge just took a few seconds; he had all these books out in front of him..." Half the judges are paedophiles, anyway; they all dress up like babies and get beaten up by madams. My mate who was a tattooist, he knew this barrister who would go in there and get his arse tattooed and there was no ink, just to... 'cause he liked it, and I'm thinking, "Well, that's not normal." So, I got taken down from court and they said, "Yeah, yeah, your barrister'll be with you in a minute, he'll explain what happened." Anyway, he never turned up; he's gone. I was like, "Great!"' Ben rolls his eyes. 'So I waited in this room for an hour. Anyway, eventually someone explained to me when I got to Elmley – it's the first jail I went to for that crime – they said, "What you get then, mate?" I said, "Five years", and he goes, "No you didn't, you're a lifer." I says, "No, he give me five years." So he got this piece of paper, spun it round and shot it across the table at me, and it said, *99 years*. My heart went...' Ben makes a sound like a bass drum.

'Ninety-nine years?'

'Yeah, I was like, I'm never, ever, getting out. And he goes, "It would say *999 years*, mate, but the computer only goes up to ninety-nine." An IPP: a sentence of Indeterminate Public Protection. What they do is, if you're a danger to the public... 'cause my violence was getting worse... Have you seen the film *Minority Report*?'

'No, sorry.'

'Well it's sci-fi, set in the future, and the police, they have these three people lying in a sort of think tank – a kind of pool – and they see the future and tell the police about crimes that are going to happen and they arrest you before you do the crime. This sentence was like that; they lock you up before you can do it. Anyway, so the guard says, "This is an *indeterminate* public protection sentence." He goes, "If you don't do what you've got to, you'll never, ever get out."

'So there I was. I hated the person I had become. I wanted to change, but it was too late; I'd just been sent to prison for nine hundred and ninety-nine years.' Ben clears his throat, and shakes his head, as if trying to shake the gloom out of his mind. 'The guard goes, "The *good* thing is, though, you'll get a single cell." Then they lock me up with two other people. One was a young lad; one was an old boy who was in for drink-driving and he snored when he was *awake*. The young lad used to piss all over the toilet seat. We was three people locked up in a two-man cell 'cause the prison was overcrowded. Eventually I *did* get a single cell and most of my prison life was in a single cell. They sent me off to Brixton. Oh, lovely! The screws... my mum come and visit me and she said to them, "You've got to get him out of here!"'

'What was so awful about it?'

'It's all the junkies and lowlife scumbags on this wing.'

'So there's a of hierarchy of criminals?'

'Yeah, so at the bottom are people who harm children, or women. And this lot are just pure scum, filth, they'd rob a man of his last pound just to get a fix, or people without feelings, or who think they're special. I was worried when I went there, 'cause it's a London jail, y'know, gangsters and Yardies in there. So one of the Yardies says, "Wanna see a picture of my victim?" And I go, "Go on, then", and it's a picture of a bloke wrapped up in a plastic bag with a bullet hole in him and boot marks stamped all over him. They're like a different category of criminal there. It's different; they're scarier if you like. But I look the part; I don't look like I'm a pushover, so people didn't really hassle me. My cell mate, he says, "It doesn't matter who you are, how big you are, how strong you are – if anyone comes and tries to pick on you, fight them. Win or lose, they won't come back because then they'll know you're a pain in the arse." If they go into a cell and try to nick someone's stuff and the person cowers in the corner, every day they'll come in and they'll take their stuff.'

'Did anyone try it on?'

'Once, but I stood my ground. There was one fella there; I think he had mental illnesses. He just went peculiar on me. I hadn't done nothing to him, nothing at all, so it was like this silverback gorilla come into my cell, fucking great... huge, just huge, this bloke, so I had a China plate, and I'm washing it up in the sink, and I'm thinking, "Well, if it goes off, I'm gonna smash the plate and stick it in his throat." I know that sounds horrible, but it's survival; it's that, or he'd stick me through the wall. But, luckily, that didn't happen. And the screws are on at me, and I'm like, "I don't know what you're on about, I haven't done nothing to him." I said, "He's mad." He was locked up. I mean, we was allowed out, but he was locked up because he was an absolute nuisance to everyone, so the officers locked him up for his own safety.

'Then I ended up in Wormwood Scrubs, and I was so upset when I left, because I made some good friends in there. And one lad I was quite good friends with, he does art, and he painted his whole cell. Screws hated it 'cause you're not s'posed to do that, but it was brilliant. We used to go in there and play cards. A good bunch of lads, not doing anything wrong, just enjoying the moment, y'know? Making the best of a bad situation. I was quite upset that I left. And then, so I went to High Down...'

'I'm amazed you can remember them all. What's with all the moving around?'

"Cause every time I went to court, someone took my space. Once I spent the night in a police cell; there was three of us, because there was no room in the prison...'

'So why did you keep going back to court?'

'First time, they read out what you've done and say whether they're gonna remand you or let you out on bail. The second time... so then it's the magistrate's, then to another magistrate's then it goes to crown, then eventually I think I done seven different jails. Yeah, so all over the South of England. Luckily they never put me in Liverpool or Scotland, 'cause that wouldn't have been... a southerner up there is...' Ben laughs, knowingly. 'So when I got sentenced, I ended up in Lewes. This is the new beginning for me, because when I step through the doors, this lady gives me a book, and it's Allen Carr's *The Easy Way to Control Alcohol*. I read it and it changed my life. So, I thought, "I'm gonna make this work", you know?'

Araminta nods and smiles, warmly.

Ben smiles back. 'I tried my hardest to get on an alcohol course. I knew I had a history with it and the blackouts. That was a very big problem; to be capable of doing something and not know what you've actually done. They didn't do a course just for drinking; they only did a drugs and alcohol course. So I went and spoke to these people and they said, "Yeah, yeah, but have you got any drug issues?" And I'm like, "Yeah, I smoke a lot of weed." But I didn't; I just wanted to get on the course. Anyway, it didn't sit right with me, so I went back to see them, and said, "I lied to you yesterday, I haven't got a drug issue, but I want to go on a course." And they was like, "Thanks for your honesty, but now you can't go on the course." But I dunno, I got a lot of information, a lot of books, a lot of reading and I worked on myself. So the Allen Carr book helped, 'cause it give me an insight. Anyway, yeah, so eventually they tell me they're starting up an alcohol group, and I thought, "Fantastic! This is good, right?"

'So I'm on this course and this woman's holding it, but she was teetotal, so I said, "Hang on a minute, I appreciate that you do a course, but you don't know where I'm coming from, 'cause you've never been there." And she said, "I know what I'm doing; I've been to college..." But I'm, like, "But you've not got the life experience." When I come out of jail, they wanted me to become a counsellor, and I thought about it, but you have to go on courses to train up to be a counsellor, and I was, like, d'you know what, I've got enough going on in my life. If I could just be me and walk into a class of people, and express myself... I'm quite happy with that, and it'd probably be, y'know, they'd listen. Some of the courses I went to and the write-ups; the things I got, I was like, brilliant, y'know? So some of the open prisons I was in... I had to go to courses on the outside. It was kinda like a day out. All the rest of the people on the course, fourteen of them, was people on the outside. And I was the best one in there.'

'In what way were you the best? The most interested? Keen?'

'Yeah, punctual, everything... they used to say to the others, "This fella, who comes from the jail and has to get a minibus and a train and walk, and he can make it on time, why can't you?" I was always involved in the conversations and the role play, 'cause I wanted to be, 'cause I wanted to change myself. Which I did. Some of the courses, when they was finished, I was upset they was finished 'cause I used to enjoy them. I had an objective: I wanted to change. So, I don't think prison works, because you have to be in a jail long enough to get on a course, and they keep moving you around. But at the end of the day, it's down to the individual if they want to change... and I did, and I have, so...

'Then my first parole come up after being in jail for two and a half years, and of course I think, "I'm getting out! I'm getting out!" Erm... but no; no mention of mitigating circumstances, and it's, "Nah, you're not getting out." And I think, "Well, I've done all your courses, been a model prisoner..."

Then the third parole hearing, the judge brought it up – what had caused it; made me do that – and he was brilliant, and they let me out on parole.

'So then I got out, and that was scary. Couldn't cross the road. Cars seemed like they was doing fifty, sixty miles an hour, but they was only doing thirty! I hadn't seen a car, for like, four years. So, whoever I met, they was like, "Come on then, let's go out." And I was like, "I can't; I can't cross the road; they're going too fast!" And how rude people are! When I got out, I was so shocked. I was busting to meet people, 'cause I thought people in jail was rude; they're not rude. They're not like outside people. I'd open doors for 'em and they wouldn't say thank you.' Ben laughs.

'Can you remember anything that you learned on any of these courses that really helped; that really sat with you?'

'Yeah, I s'pose one thing is noticing your trigger points when you're getting angry. They used to say to me, "How d'you know when you're angry?" I said, "I don't, I just get angry." They said, "Well, no..." I thought about it, and I thought, "Well, I clench my teeth." And they said, "Next time you get angry look in the mirror."'

'So what d'you do? Notice yourself angry, and then what do you do?'

'When I was in Swaleside, I changed from a Roman Catholic to a Buddhist and, in prison, they'd be angry all around me and I'd suck it all in, but then I'd go back to my cell and meditate and release all their anger; breathe it all out. It's not a religion, it's a belief, so you put in and take out what you want. Some of the things they teach, I still do. I wish I did it a bit more. I should really try doing it again, but I don't really get angry these days. But it's still nice sometimes to sit in a quiet place and meditate. That's why I go night fishing.'

'Night fishing?'

'Yeah, I'm going this weekend. I'm going to this lake; it's beautiful. It's like being in another country. It's near Rochester; the Blue Lake. So you imagine, you get there in the morning, and you set up your bivvy – that's a little tent; a bivouac – your rods are out... so you're watching all the daylight changing; the sun coming up, going down. At night, the shadows, reflections...'

'How long are you planning to be there?'

'This one I'm gonna go for twenty-four hours.'

'So it's not about the fishing; it's about being somewhere peaceful?'

'Yeah, I just love it. There's no people about. I mean, I go with me mate, but it's just beautiful. Peace and quiet.'

Ben shows Araminta a photo on his phone of a magically-turquoise lake.

'It's so blue! Why is it so blue?'

'It's a chalk pit. That blue – that's why I say it's like being in another country.'

Ben scrolls through his photos again. Araminta tries to reconcile the Ben who beat up a man so badly he put him in hospital, with the Ben who'd just spent the morning helping a lonely old lady.

'What strikes me about your life is that every time you got in really bad trouble you were actually trying to help somebody vulnerable. You have a big heart.'

'Yeah, massive heart; just a shit life. No love; no love as a child from my parents, so I s'pose I craved love; I wanted there to be love in the world.' Ben shrugs. 'Still, here I am now, enjoying life, and going to the Blue Lake, night fishing this weekend. Gonna watch the sunset, watch the sunrise.'

'I can picture you, in your tent, disappearing into the darkness as the sun sets over the lake...'

'I've got photos of that.' Ben scrolls down on his phone. 'And there's these, too. Look at it in the morning, when the sun comes up.'

Araminta looks at Ben's photo of turquoise water with gentle ripples topped in molten gold.

'Come on', says Ben, 'I'll put that battery in for you'.

'I'd almost forgotten about the battery!'

***

Araminta watches Ben saunter back down the hill. She wonders whether she and Ben are now friends. She can't imagine herself night fishing with him, or playing cards with him in a prison cell.

Beatrice, Araminta's neighbour opposite, comes into sight, strolling back from the park in her Hunter boots and Barbour. Beatrice, whose perfect life somehow makes Araminta feel nervous. Divorced, maybe, but then aren't half of us? And her son with the posh name: Hugo. Hugo, with his successful job in television. Beatrice, who had inherited her father's legal firm. Beatrice, on the right side of the law while Ben is firmly on the other, now struggling to make ends meet while working on roofs – the only job probation had been able to get him. If you swapped their childhoods, would it be Ben in the Hunter Boots and Barbour, and Beatrice in grey prison issue sweatshirt and joggers? Where's the justice in that?

As he reaches the bend in the road, Ben turns and waves to Araminta. She feels a warm tingle in her face as she smiles and waves, too. Yes, she's made a new friend.

Back in her house, she walks into the kitchen, reaches for her small blue teapot, and remembers she was supposed to be driving to Waitrose to buy leaf tea. She'll have to have something else, but she doesn't care. It's definitely worth going without leaf tea to get to know Ben. If his story has taught her anything, it's that a leopard absolutely *can* change its spots.

15 Secret Street – Denise

Sixteen weeks before the Platinum Jubilee street party

Araminta's doorbell clangs its Westminster chime, and she swings open her front door to find her neighbour, Denise. Denise can't be so very much younger than Araminta. She's wearing fuchsia pink boots, a bold, bright, orange needlecord dress, and has dyed-blond short hair, which she wears swept back from her face with a multicoloured floral hairband. She looks like spring, personified.

'I don't want to disturb you, but I felt I had to come round and apologise.'

Araminta furrows her brow. 'Whatever for?'

'Arthur got a bit excited last night, with the football.'

'Oh, I see. You don't need to worry about that; I love to hear him shouting when his team scores. It breaks up the silence in my living room.'

'Well, we didn't want to be annoying you.'

'No, it's lovely. I picture him punching the air when he yells, "Yesss!"

Denise laughs. 'That's exactly what he does!'

'It's very nice of you to come and apologise, though, even though it's not necessary.' Araminta smiles.

'And also, your street party invitation', says Denise. 'What a lovely idea! Arthur and I will be there. Well, I will definitely.'

'Oh, good; I'm looking forward to it already.'

'I used to work for them once.'

'Sorry?'

'The Royal Family.'

'No!' Araminta's eyes widen. This is fabulous; a chance to get to know her neighbour better – maybe even make another friend – *and* to hear about her beloved Royal Family. 'Do you have time to come in and tell me about it?'

'Now?'

'Yes, if you can?' Araminta gestures for Denise to come in and Denise obediently follows.

Araminta's living room is capacious, wallpapered in gold and cream vertical stripes, with a white dado rail and ornate coving. A Waterford Crystal chandelier hangs from a central ceiling rose. There's a white marble fireplace surround, with tiles depicting stylish wreaths and urns, and on the mantelpiece, a collection of Royal Crown Derby gilt-decorated figurines: pheasants, a nuthatch, a robin, a goldfinch, hares, and a penguin. Jostling for space are two silver-framed photographs. One, a studio family portrait of a middle-aged woman, partner and young adult children; the other a couple in their fifties wearing bush tucker hats, shorts, and short-sleeved shirts, posing in front of the iconic red sandstone rock, Uluru, in central Australia. On the wall above the fireplace is a large silver-framed coronation portrait of the Queen seated in Westminster Abbey, wearing her crown, and holding her ceremonial orb and sceptre. Her Majesty looks regal, but also somehow vulnerable. Arranged in a horseshoe shape are three wide yellow damask Knowle sofas, each with their high sides held up with gold-coloured rope binding palatial upholstered knobs at the back. There's a large, yellow silk rug, on which stands a polished walnut coffee table.

'Have a seat, and I'll grab us a coffee.' Araminta walks to the kitchen and returns with a tray bearing a Bodum cafetière, two porcelain beakers, a sugar bowl, milk jug, and two silver spoons in a little dish. 'Would you like a shortbread?'

'D'you know, there *was* a time when I would have said, "No I can't; I'm on a diet." But then I read that Susie Orbach book, *On Eating*, and threw away my bathroom scales. My excess weight fell off without me even thinking about it.'

'Oh! How does that work?'

'I think I was obsessed with weighing myself, every morning, then I would tell myself I must diet that day, and then all I could think about was food.'

'It obviously works, because you look great.'

'Thanks. So I'm asking myself, would I like a shortbread, and I'm thinking, actually, I'd rather just have the coffee on its own.'

'And if you were on a diet, you'd have a piece?'

'Yes, because then I'd feel bad that I'm not allowed it, and want it!'

'Now you put it like that, I'm not sure I want one, either', says Araminta. 'I only get them out to be polite.'

'See, it works', says Denise. 'Anyway, here I am going on about *not* dieting, and you want me to tell you all about working at Buckingham Palace.'

'Yes!' says Araminta, and rubs her hands together, excitedly.

'Yes, well, I was very young; it was a long time ago.'

'What did you do there?'

'Only a maid. A lowly maid. But I used to be there holding Princess Margaret's ashtray sometimes, at functions. I was her "human ashtray".'

'Oh, my goodness, I cannot believe we've lived next door to each other all this time and I didn't know!'

'When I landed the job of daily maid at Kensington Palace, Mum and Dad were so proud – their little princess working for a princess. I thought it would be glamorous. Ladies-in-waiting have to be aristocrats, and I was just a daily maid; an art history graduate from Clapham. I wasn't paid much, just minimum wage. Still, though, I suppose at least I wasn't a dull old cleaner in someone's house; I was a maid in a palace.'

'Oh, tell all!'

'The thing is, when I was little, with my mousy brown hair in bunches and my Mary-Jane shoes, my favourite book was the Ladybird book, *Cinderella*. I dreamed of being Cinders, in a golden carriage on the way to meet my prince at the ball. Oh to have a pink silk ballgown and dainty glass slippers. I mean, *glass* slippers! I couldn't think of anything more exotic. It never crossed my mind that glass slippers might shatter.'

'You mean being a princess isn't all it's cracked up to be?' Araminta asks.

'Yes, exactly. I mean, was my palace job really so glamorous?'

'Surely it was?'

'Well, there were strange rules. No vacuuming before ten in the morning, to allow the Royals to rest. No walking down the centre of the corridor carpets so as not to wear them out with our commoners' feet. We had to behave as if we didn't exist, and to them, we didn't. I didn't get to go into Margaret's bedroom; I wasn't far enough up the servants' hierarchy, but there were tales that people – male servants – walked in on her, sitting at her dressing table stark naked, and she didn't bat an eyelid. That's how invisible we were.'

Araminta gasps, then says, 'Go on; I don't want to interrupt your flow'.

'Well, Margaret stayed in bed each morning till ten, chain-smoking and reading the papers, which she dropped on the floor for staff to pick up later. Then downstairs for a vodka pick-me-up, then a cocktail before lunch. I would have been off my head with that much alcohol inside me at that time of day. Her drinking and smoking were legendary, of course. I didn't see it, but they say she even tried gluing matchboxes to whiskey tumblers so she could enjoy even more Chesterfields with her Famous Grouse. She often chain-smoked, though, lighting one off another. My job in the evenings was to follow her round with an ashtray, watching the ash on her cigarette grow precariously longer and longer, always alert to which side of her it was likely to fall. If I got it wrong and missed, the ash would simply fall in a hopeless little heap on the Axminster carpet. There she was in a beautiful silk gown, cornflower blue to match her eyes, sucking on a solid gold cigarette holder, filling her lungs with tar. I'll never forget, at school, in biology, the teacher wanted us to know what smoking was doing to our bodies, unseen, inside of us. She brought in a pair of pig's lungs, spread newspaper on the science lab counter, flopped the browny-pink lungs down, then splashed them with black paint. I used to think of that when I caught Margaret's ash.'

'Poor Margaret.'

'Poor Margaret? Hmm... Did Margaret really deserve all this?'

This isn't the opinion Araminta was hoping for. 'Does deserving have anything to do with it, or is it all about the royal line; the blood line? You don't have to *do* anything to be royal; you just are. Ignoring the servants is surely part of the job description.'

'Well, there's a way of doing it. You don't have to be rude. In many ways she was a nasty piece of work; clearly jealous of her big sister.'

'But surely that's natural? Her sister got to have a decent education; she got to be Second Subaltern Elizabeth Alexandra Mary Windsor, wearing a uniform, playing with army trucks...' says Araminta.

'Well, yes, I suppose it's fair to say it must have been hard for Margaret that her big sister was Queen. "Margaret always wants what I have", Elizabeth said. Margaret tried to create a role for herself as a fashion icon, but I don't think that really worked.'

'Oh, but she was known as as "the party princess"', says Araminta, frowning.

Denise smiles. 'You know so much about her!'

'Yes, the Royal Family have always been important to me. As a child, I listened to them on the wireless... "Wireless!" Hark at me, as old as a dinosaur. Anyway, yes, it was hard for Margaret. She was the "spare". All she had was beauty; young girls drooling at her New Look fashions in fizzing sherbet colours, a dainty, cinched-in waist, and a flouncing skirt.'

'Was she a fashion icon? Or just a clothes horse?' says Denise. 'Did she think she could be like Audrey Hepburn? Did she really think she could be Bohemian? Who was she kidding? She was just a lonely, lost little rich kid.'

Araminta wanted to make a friend; not have an argument with her neighbour. Perhaps she shouldn't have invited Denise in. She tries to see Denise's point of view. 'Maybe she never quite found her place, if you see what I mean; she never seemed comfortable in her own skin.'

'She put everyone on edge when she entered the room', says Denise. 'Even her motorbike-riding photographer husband rejected her. That marriage was doomed from the beginning, and burnt out almost as quickly as her Chesterfields.'

'Aren't you being unfair on her?' says Araminta. 'Wasn't she a lovesick, heartbroken victim, unable to marry her dashing equerry, Group Captain Peter Townsend, because of her beloved sister's position as Queen...'

'And Defender of the Faith?'

'Yes', says Araminta, '*and* Supreme Governor of the Church of England, too'.

'But she knew exactly what she was doing when she intimately brushed that piece of fluff from Townsend's shoulder on Coronation Day! She knew she was in full view of the paparazzi and likely to upstage her sister.'

'Wasn't she simply so in love, she was unable to help herself touching him? She had to call off their marriage because of a sense of duty to the crown and church', says Araminta.

'Or', says Denise, 'was she actually just bored with him? The author, Selina Hastings, said Peter Townsend was "wet". Wasn't Margaret simply shallow; unwilling to give up her royal privileges and become a plain old suburban housewife?'

Araminta thinks friendships are simply too much trouble. Perhaps she'd been right not to bother much with people since she retired. She pushes the plunger down on the cafetière.

'Margaret could be *so* mean', says Denise. 'She said Boy George looked like an over made-up tart, and refused to be photographed with him at a radio DJ awards ceremony. Boy George was only twenty-two. That was cruel. Then there's the story of her making an ambassador kneel in front of her and wipe her skirt where he'd accidentally splashed sauce. So – to answer the question of whether she was a nasty piece of work or a lovelorn heroine – my golden rule is to forget a person's status, or their personal beauty, or history, and just feel how the room changes when they walk in. And here it is: as I said before, she made everyone feel on edge. It was as if we were fish in a tank, and someone had just dropped in a piranha.'

Araminta wonders how the room changes when she enters it. Could people somehow, instinctively feel she's uncomfortable in her own skin? It makes her feel even more gloomy. If so, it isn't her fault, though, surely? 'The thing is', she says, 'I feel sorry for Margaret. She wasn't born to be the Queen's sister; that happened suddenly and unexpectedly when her superficial, vain, Nazi-supporting uncle abdicated so he could marry the divorcée, Wallis Simpson. Suddenly her beloved father and sister had to leave their close-knit family's home.'

'Yes, they referred to themselves as "us four", didn't they?' says Denise.

'Yes, and she was left to rattle around Clarence House with her bitter and grumpy mother. So, it's easy to say if she'd really loved Townsend she would have given up her civil list income, her royal titles, and been happy to be a suburban housewife, but how could she undermine her big sister when, at that time, it was expressly forbidden for divorced people to be married in church?'

'You're right', says Denise. 'Vows in church were considered to have been made before God, and people took that sort of thing more seriously back then.'

'They absolutely did. I wish they took it a bit more seriously now', says Araminta, then immediately wishes she hadn't. She doesn't want Denise to start wondering about her "dear departed Frederick". She quickly starts talking again. 'There was so much trauma caused to that little family by their uncle abdicating, she couldn't just abdicate herself, could she? They say when Churchill, egged on by Clemmie, had Townsend exiled; sent away to be air attaché to the British Embassy in Brussels before she could say goodbye, Margaret couldn't bear it. She collapsed like a house of cards'.

'It's true they were friends for life; Margaret and Peter', says Denise.

'That surely shows', says Araminta, 'that the marriage would have worked. He came to see her for the final time just before she died'.

'That's actually very sad.'

They sip their coffees. The aroma is rich and tangy.

'Margaret *could* be kind if she put her mind to it', says Denise, thoughtfully. 'I heard she paid for private surgery for the wife of one of her chefs.'

Araminta hopes Denise's attitude is softening a little. Perhaps they *can* be friends. 'Her long-time lady-in-waiting...'

'Anne Glenconner?' asks Denise.

'Yes, Anne, who knew her as well as anyone, always praised her and said Margaret was misunderstood', says Araminta. 'And she was treated for depression. They found her a psychiatrist from the Priory.'

'Maybe if you have the best every day, there's nothing to look forward to. It isn't a treat, is it, if you do it every day? Then luxuries are no longer luxuries. Like a rock star who's achieved fame and, feeling there's nothing more to achieve, takes a drug overdose.'

'Perhaps you're right', says Araminta, 'maybe it feels hopeless when you're at the top of society and it still doesn't make you happy. When she overdosed on nitrazepam, Margaret said she just wanted a nice rest, but I'm not sure anyone believed her.'

'Isn't smoking a sort of long, slow suicide?' says Denise. 'Margaret knew the risks well. Her grandfather, George V, and her beloved papa, George VI, both died as a result of smoking.'

'And Margaret had a cancer scare when they took a lung biopsy in 1985.'

'Fancy you knowing the date!'

'The Royal Family has always been my main interest. And I'm so enjoying sharing it with you', says Araminta, beaming. This is a success, after all. Surely finding a shared interest with Denise and chatting to her about it in her own home means Denise is now a friend?

Araminta takes another sip of coffee. 'Thank you for coming in for coffee, Denise.'

'It's nice that you asked.'

'How long have you lived here now?'

'Well, let me think. We bought No. 15 when we moved down from Islington, so maybe about twenty years. I'm one of the early DFLs.'

Araminta smiles. She's not going to explore the subject of "Down From Londons" pushing up property prices and pricing out the locals. She doesn't want to risk this new, fragile friendship. 'It feels different, doesn't it', she says, 'inviting someone into one's home, as opposed to chatting outside?'

'Yes, I suppose it does', replies Denise, thoughtfully. 'Where were we?'

'Smoking.'

'Oh, yes, I was going to say, you know her lady-in-waiting said Margaret decided to give up smoking in 1991? Just stopped.'

'Margaret must have known by then it was far too late. Eleven years later, she died.'

'And there was I, holding her ashtray, as she smoked herself to death. You can understand, then, that even though I didn't like her, I remember being her human ashtray with sadness as well as indignation. Me in my silly little blouse and skirt, darting around her like a kind of dog-end-obsessed, idiotic eagle, but free to leave that job and do anything I liked with my long, unfettered, life.'

'Margaret, constantly sucking in smoke, lonely and lovelorn, locked into her role, and destined to always be second best; never to be Queen', says Araminta.

'They had her cremated – her raddled liver, her black-painted lungs...'

'Her broken heart...'

'All gone; turned to cinders.'

'Ash.'

The Recovery
House – Jed

Fifteen weeks before the Platinum Jubilee street party

Araminta stands at the front door of the white-rendered house, puzzling at the push-button code keypad. As she wonders which of the three bells to press beneath it, a man appears from behind her with a Tesco carrier bag.

'Which one of us are you after?'

'Oh, hello, well, any of you, really.'

The man is in his fifties with a weather-beaten face, but otherwise he looks remarkably normal in a pair of jeans and a half-zip grey jumper. Except his pale blue eyes are so startling that it occurs to Araminta that if ice could be on fire, this is what it would look like.

'Me, then. I'm Jed.' Araminta shakes Jed's hand; a firm grip.

'I'm Araminta.'

'What can I do for you?'

'Well, I would like to give you all one of these. It's an invitation to a Platinum Jubilee street party.'

'Well, thank you very much. We're supposed to be joining in with the community while we're here. Would you like to come in for a coffee? I've just bought Hobnobs.' He waves his carrier bag.

Araminta isn't sure if she *does* want to go into a rehab unit, but it doesn't feel right to say no, and she's determined to continue her quest for friends, so replies, 'How kind of you; that would be lovely'.

Jed presses four buttons on the keypad and swings the front door open to a clinical-looking white hallway, then shows Araminta into the front room, tastefully decorated with pale lavender on two walls and light grey on the others. 'Have a seat', he says, and Araminta sits on one of the three black vinyl sofas that are arranged around a plain imitation-teak coffee table.

'Won't be a minute. Sugar?'

'No, thank you for asking.' Araminta's afraid it will be instant coffee. She hates instant coffee. The room seems a little bleak; more like a waiting room than a living room in a normal home. No cushions. No ornaments. The arm of the black vinyl sofa feels cold to her touch as she sits down. There's a nice picture of a sunrise on the wall, though, with the caption, *Just for Today*. Jed returns with two plain yellow earthenware mugs of coffee and a plate of Hobnobs, which he puts on the table.

'Thanks so much', says Araminta, fishing in her handbag for the party invitations. 'I brought six. Is that right?'

'Yes, there are six of us, but also two staff.'

'Oh, I...'

'That's fine, we can share, can't we?'

'Yes, that would be great.'

Araminta realises she's sounding overly cheerful, like a primary school teacher, and frowns.

'You a bit nervous?'

'Well, I...I've never been in a rehab before, so I don't know what to expect.'

'Recovery house.'

'Sorry?'

'We don't call it a rehab; we call it a recovery house.' Araminta's struck by his voice; middle class, almost, with a bit of a Kentish twang.

'That's much nicer; that's lovely.'

'It's alright, though, I can understand your anxiety. These places feel a bit weird, don't they?'

'I suppose... well, it's your home, though.'

'For now, yes. I tell you what...' Araminta sips her instant coffee. It's delicious.

'If I tell you how I got here, you won't be anxious any more. You see, if people understand the reasons for situations that frighten them, the fear evaporates.' Araminta's fascinated.

'Yes, please do, I have plenty of free time.'

'Right then. You sitting comfortably?'

Araminta nods. 'Is it a story of addiction?'

'Mine is a story of pure and utter chaos. My mum was from quite a wealthy background. Her father was a captain in the Air Force, a pilot during World War Two, and her mother was a teacher. When Mum was sixteen, she was on the back of her boyfriend's moped – no helmets back then – and they crashed. It was autumn, and her head got rammed into a small, sharp stump left on a tree where a branch had broken off. She was in a coma for six months. Afterwards, they had to teach her to eat. It left her brain-damaged; disabled. You can tell my mum that a fifty-foot pink marshmallow's floating down in the street outside right now and it's going to be our Sunday lunch, and she'll believe it. I don't think she'd have got together with Dad if she hadn't been so trusting. Dad was a chronically bad-tempered violent version of Frank Spencer.'

'I remember him! The hapless fool with the beret? What was that sitcom?'

'*Some Mothers do 'Ave 'Em.* Yeah, living with him was like living with a hand grenade with the pin pulled. Anyway, Dad got her pregnant, and back then it just wasn't done to be pregnant out of wedlock, so Mum's family married them off. My mum being a strict Catholic, divorce was never an option. Dad was incredibly selfish. He used to spend all Mum's disability benefits on himself. For instance, he was into electronics, and bought himself a top-of-the-range oscilloscope, which cost about four or five grand. He had the latest radios, and a signal generator – really nice piece of kit – sitting under his bed. He had a new pair of shoes imported. They cost several hundred quid. Meanwhile we went to school in rags.

'We were a family of four scruffy kids with unruly, mahogany brown curly hair, living at the Pantiles, in an enormous maisonette that Mum and Dad rented from the council. We traded scrap metal, which was often heaped up in the living room. My family's idea of washing was that we'd have a bath at Christmas, and that's only if your feet stank.'

Araminta can't stop herself grimacing.

'Yeah.' Jed laughs. 'Think Stig of the Dump. Think Worzel Gummidge. We had two massive open log fires, so, because Mum was disabled and Dad was too bleedin' lazy to get out of bed, my older brother and I weren't allowed to go to school until we'd built the fire. If we were short of wood, we'd go to the woods on the Common. I've been swinging a ten-pound sledgehammer, using axes and wedges since I was ten; a chainsaw since I was twelve. Once we were gathering wood and the police came along, asking, "What are you lot up to? What's a twelve-year-old doing with a chainsaw?"'

Araminta tries to imagine a small boy revving up a heavy chainsaw with an angry-looking blade.

'Dad wouldn't give us the bus fare to get to school, so we used to go to High Brooms tip and forage for bits and pieces to build bicycles. Where my leg rubbed against the chain, there was grease all down my school trousers, and I remember getting changed for games one day and I had a bicycle chain imprinted on my leg. We got handouts, and clothes from charity shops. That was only because teachers sent letters home saying, *Do something about this now!* I remember – I hated games – I didn't want to get changed for sports because the only underwear I had was Mum's. You can imagine a thirteen-year-old boy in the school changing rooms wearing his mum's knickers. Of course I got bullied. They called me "Bloomers".'

Araminta pictures him as a scruffy, ostracised boy in a playground, taunted with this horrible nickname. Did he cry? Run away? Fight? 'I'm so sorry that happened to you', she says.

'Crime coming out of our ear 'oles. Police coming round all the time. Social services put me on probation. It was one step before borstal. I was getting arrested all the time for breaking into cars; criminal damage... I spent an entire year bunking off school. I left with one CSE, and that was only because I got caught in town by the metalwork teacher and he marched me into the exam. I aced that because we were doing scrap metal construction at home. I was using an oxyacetylene gas cutting machine at twelve! We cleared scrap metal for people. We'd be asked to get rid of unwanted old cars, or farm machinery from farms, or stuff from building sites. We'd cut them up, stick the bits in the back of the van, then drive them to scrap yards to sell. Sometimes we'd take bits of metal home to cut up. Dad would get us to forage around in skips for bits of old scrap metal, too. We were doing motor mechanics; all kinds of stuff. Our childhood was completely loopy. A typical scene would be us kids in a field cutting up a combine harvester, and our brain-damaged, disabled mum using the gas cutting set. We were scavengers, as if we were living in a post-apocalyptic world.

'Dad met this guy; Shaun. He was six foot seven, highly intelligent; an electronics engineer, and he taught me electronics. Our downstairs lounge was more like Ground Control. We had transmitters; we had scanners... One of the times when I was arrested, we knew the police were coming, because we got it on the scanner. We had a forty-foot mast with aerials that rotated on top of the chimney. We were transmitting to Australia! You could go up and sit on Wellington Rocks, look down, and see the top of our aerial moving round.

'Dad was very violent towards us; a classic bully. I don't want to say much more about that, though. Still, as we grew up, one by one we hit him back, and he started leaving us alone.'

Araminta wants to say something helpful, but can't think of anything, so just nods.

As if to try and cheer her up, Jed says, 'Mum comes up with real gems. Once Dad was giving one of his stories from when he was in the Royal Engineers; a war story of when he was in Africa, and this battle, and I said to Dad, "So where were you at this point?" and Mum shouts from the kitchen, "Running in the opposite direction!"'

Araminta laughs.

'When I left school, I got into the electronics that Shaun was teaching me, then started a college course in Tonbridge. I excelled at it; it was second nature to me. Then when I was introduced to the study of sound; whoa! I took off like a rocket. I'm qualified now to transmit around the world. You know how Britain found out that the Falklands had been invaded? From a guy in the Falklands; a radio ham enthusiast?'

'It rings a bell.'

'I've got that qualification. I worked for a company in Brighton, designing in-car entertainment systems; sound systems. These things were – back in '93/'94 – up to about £200 for a stereo system; this was top-end stuff. I used to get radios from work and fit them for people at the pub for fifty quid. Nice side line.

'It was about then I got into drugs. I had no social skills, and I started smoking cannabis – solids – because I thought it made me more interesting. I had a girlfriend, Dawn. You might think this is insensitive and rude, but she was thick. I loved her, but she just bored the shit out of me. I had no ability to talk to people, really, but when I came across cannabis, I found it gave me something interesting to say. I spent about two years smoking that, until I realised that all I was doing was spending every day in bed. I was addicted, and stopped that, but then cross-addicted to amphetamine. Amphetamine bit me; dug its teeth right in. I started injecting it, an eighth at a time. A gram will keep most people going for twenty-four hours. I was banging up three and a half grams in one hit. I would start walking; just point, pick a line, and go in that direction; just keep going. I crossed streams and rivers and housing estates and building sites and motorways and bypasses and people's gardens... Once I started in Eastbourne and ended up in London in a doorway, thinking, "How the bloody hell did I get here?" I'd walked non-stop for three days and three nights.

'The begging started when I was at a mate's house and we were bored and had no money. It was only a tenner for a bag of speed.

'The thing about addiction for me was altering my perspective. People always describe my blue eyes as "piercing"; it's as if I see the world differently from everyone else. I remember larking about in my bedroom as a kid and climbing on furniture because I wanted to see things from a new angle. I found drugs did that for me. A different philosophical angle; a different perception.'

'Can you give an example, so I understand better?'

'Messing with morality's one example. It swept preconceived social ideas out of the way. I felt as if I'd been beamed down from another planet to Earth and I had to fathom out what was going on. I really enjoyed that. I've always had this weird fascination with how things work, and it doesn't matter whether it's a biro, a car, a washing machine, an escalator, or a human. It's an obsession of mine, and it was like that with reality. I wrote a poem about it when I first got into recovery. D'you want to hear it?'

Araminta really doesn't, but nods, enthusiastically.

'Addiction

I think I have an allergy –
I don't like reality.
Or is that just analogy;
a twisted metaphor
for alcoholic depravity?'

'An allergy to reality', says Araminta. 'Brilliant, I can relate to that!'

Jed smiles. 'I've done five prison sentences; the longest one eighteen months. Mine is a *very* long record. I was stood in court one day (this was about five years ago in Hastings), on a charge of drunk and disorderly. The magistrate asked – in that poncy voice they use – "What are the previous convictions?" The prosecution stood up and said, "I'm not reading them out, but there are eighty-seven of them." That's not including motoring offences; thirteen disqualifications from driving. Right now I'm on a three-year probation order, a three-year ASBO; I'm not allowed to have an open vessel of alcohol, or beg, anywhere in Kent. That's my second ASBO in Kent. I've been begging on and off for thirty years, and I've never actually been done for it. I got hassled in Hastings for that – aggressive begging – when I first became homeless. One day there's this police officer having a go at me, so I thought, "OK, I'm not allowed to ask for money, I'll start singing!" I thought I'd come over all Oliver Twist, and I sang, "Spare any change? Got any change?"'

Jed sings beautifully. His singing voice is easily good enough for a West End musical, Araminta thinks.

'Everybody knew that I was just conning the policeman, but he couldn't do anything because I was busking; not begging. You see the problem is, me and crime... you know the expression, "Rules are for the obedience of fools and the guidance of wise men"?'

Araminta nods, vaguely.

'If you don't understand the rule; follow it anyway, 'cause it's probably good for you. But if you can understand the rule, then question it, and only follow it if you think it's of use. I've extended that saying: "... because it takes a wise man to realise he's a fool." The French sociologist, Durkheim, came up with the idea of Functionalism: everything in society's there for a purpose. Well, crime and deviance serves a purpose, and he said that society needs to evolve, because if it stagnates, it dies, and social evolution comes from breaking the rules. So I tend to only follow the rules that I think make sense. So, currently, yeah, probation, ASBO, twenty-eight-day curfew, treatment requirements, a £400 fine... I've been breaking the law since I was twelve.'

Araminta's starting to feel lost in this parallel universe; Jed's world where the normal rules don't apply. She nibbles a Hobnob and drains her coffee cup.

'Would you like another one? Another coffee?'

'Well, why not? That was delicious.'

'Aldi.'

'Hwhat?' At the mention of a budget brand, Araminta finds herself involuntarily upping the posh accent.

'Aldi. Just instant.'

'Goodness! The only thing with all this coffee drinking is that I could do with visiting the lavatory.'

Jed stands up, and says, 'Follow me', showing her to an open door in the hallway. Inside is a small, white painted cubicle with hand basin and toilet. Above the basin is a sign that makes Araminta smile: *PRACTISE MINDFUL URINATION*.

She returns to the living room as Jed is coming back in with fresh coffees. 'So you were talking about breaking the law...'

'Yes', says Jed, as they sit down again. 'In 1998 my probation officer said, "Right, I've got to write a report on you, and I want you to go to this hostel – a probation place up in Yorkshire. You can either go to that, and stop taking drugs, or I recommend that you go to prison." So I took the easy option. I got put on a deferred sentence. If I did well, I stood a chance of staying out of prison. If I messed about, I was definitely going to prison. Because of my record, and the length of it, they assigned the manager, Vicky, as my probation officer. One day I went into the office because I had three different pre-sentence reports, all saying different stuff, and I asked, "Look, which one's right?" She said, "Well, you've stopped taking drugs, you're bored, why don't you go and find out? Go and study something." So I went to the local college with my reports, and asked, "What do I do to get my head around this?" They advised me to study GCSE sociology and psychology. So I started them, and I really got into it.

'Vicky was about five foot five with long, dark hair, and dressed like a social worker – Doc Martens with jeans, or long, cotton skirts. She had a practical way of doing things, which made sense to me, and she had this way about her that made me feel calm. Somehow she was able to make me behave responsibly. We had similar views about the absurdities of the system, and as we railed against it together, we became close, and ended up becoming a couple. Then Vicky became pregnant, and we got kicked out of the hostel. Probation got really angry. They wanted to send her off to London; tried to buy her a fur coat.'

'I haven't heard that expression for ages. Buy her off, you mean; pay her to leave?'

'Yeah. And they tried stitching me up in court with the report. Vicky obviously got asked to leave her job and she said to me, "What are we gonna do for money?" I said, "Well, you've got more qualifications than me, so go and do a degree." She did. We moved into family accommodation provided by the university.

'When our daughter was born, we called her Lydia. It means 'beautiful one'. She was – she is – beautiful; the only thing I've got right in my entire life. I was a stay-at-home dad and studied part-time, and Vicky was full-time. My younger brother, Neil, joined us, and started studying psychiatry. (He went on to become a CPN: Community Psychiatric Nurse.) So we were all students together. When Vicky finished her degree, we swapped, and I started my psychology degree, because I'd done A levels by then. She started working in social services as a counselling psychologist, and then got a job in the prison as a psychotherapist.

'Anyway, when I'd got together with Vicky, I'd stopped drugs, and slowly but surely started drinking. In the student environment with parties, and chatting in the bar after lectures, my drinking crept up and up and up. It was alcoholism that finished my relationship with Vicky. Afterwards, I got together with Heather; another alcoholic. Two alcoholics in one house was a complete nightmare; a permanent three-year row. So when Heather and I split up, I thought, "Right, that's it, I'm staying on my own, so I might as well drink as much as I like." Lydia was growing up to be an absolute legend. She has a cracking sense of humour, she's fearless, and a credit to humanity. But then Vicky wouldn't let me see Lydia. Losing access to my precious daughter broke me. I spent all day drinking, begging, drinking, begging, getting arrested, drinking... I'd lost the plot; lost the will to live. I found out recently that I'm a grandfather now to a boy and a girl. I don't know their names.'

Araminta looks at his face. His complexion seems to have turned grey. She wants to say something to make him feel better, but blurts out, 'I have three, but they live a long way away'.

Jed nods. 'I came back down South, and stayed with Mum and Dad for a bit, but of course – because of the rows with Dad – that didn't last long. I rented a flat for a while, still drinking. I got into all the legal highs. I pretended to be homeless to beg for money. I spent a long time being housed and begging. Later on, when I was truly homeless, it taught me a very big lesson, and it was a hard lesson to learn: when you are actually homeless and you *need* to beg, you hate people like I was because they're taking money out of your hands.

'The owner of the flat wanted to sell, so I had to leave. I bought an old banger of a van to live in. Then something weird happened: I took to homelessness easily. I had everything I needed. I was qualified in electronics, I'd done building work, studied psychology. And because I'd had such a feral childhood – it was just survival – all that kicked into gear. The old banger broke down, but I managed to get it to Alexandra Park in Hastings. I was there for six weeks, living in the van. At night, I dug the dirt out from under some paving slabs with a knife and buried a cable, then hooked up to a lamp post. I had a TV and a fan heater going in this van in the middle of the park. That lasted until a dog walker caught his foot in one of the paving stones where my cable had lifted it a bit, and found the cable, so he called the police.

'I lived in a caravan for an entire year. That was in West St. Leonards; Bo Peep, the coach park road. Solar panel in the back; big thing. Had a TV going in that, too. I was there for a year. Had a deal going with the police and the council. They would allow me to live there in the caravan if I didn't go into town and beg. In the end it got invaded by heroin addicts, so that was the end of that.

'A big part of me enjoyed being homeless. There were no rules. I remember when we used to hang out in Tunbridge Wells in the boarded-up doorway where BHS used to be. There were five of us: "Posh Pam" (nutter of a woman – grew up in a swanky mansion in Neville Park); "Bilko" (who used to be a sergeant in the army); "Digger" (because his initials were JCB); "Mullet" (due to his hairstyle, of course), and; yours truly. All alkies. We had a good time, y'know? There were parts of homelessness that were brilliant fun. It was like I was housed, but in the open air. I had everything I needed. If I wanted to charge my phone, I'd just go to an electric shop, or a lamp post, or a train or something. If I needed clothes, well, there's a charity shop, that'd do. And there was the soup run at the car park. I think it was a case of cutting a suit according to the cloth you've got. Because that was my childhood; I just had to get on with it.'

'Is this what they call "entrenched" homelessness?'

'Yeah, I suppose it is. One of the things I liked was going to Sainsbury's, "borrowing" steaks, picking a piece of metal – an old foil takeaway container, or something like that – out of a bin to make a barbeque. Then I'd go up to the Common, bung a radio on, have a couple of beers, and build a camp fire, bring my friends. There were people milling around; I didn't care about them; just put the steak on to cook. I'd look at those people staring at us, and I'd think, "I'm having a beer and a steak and listening to Radio 4, what are you up to?"

'There's a new-build, where the old Kent & Sussex Hospital used to be, just off St. John's. At the back of this block of flats, there's a six-bay car park, and me and Bilko were kipping there, under a bike shelter. One day there's a rainstorm; a deluge. One of the people came out from the flats, objecting to us being there. I said to them, "Get on with it, call the police, I don't bloody well care!" So "Chalky" – that's what we called PC White, the local beat bobby – turned up...'

'Not Toby White, at No. 98?'

'Yes! You can imagine I wasn't that happy when I came here and found out he lives in the same street. He's down the hill, though; doesn't come up here because town's in the opposite direction. Anyway, Chalky said, "Come on then, off you go!" And I said, "You think I'm going out in that? You're nuts, mate! I tell you what, though, I'll only go if there's hot food in the cell, please. And if you're gonna arrest me, bring the car closer." You know what he said? "Stay there then!" And he talked to the owner; said, "Come on! You're gonna turf him out on a night like this?" The police had already worked out that incarceration doesn't frighten me; they can't use it as a weapon. This has got a lot to do with addiction, I think. One of the things that the Fellowship says is Step One is admitting you're powerless over your addiction. I've just been doing Step One, and I have a new way of looking at that. You're *not* powerless, because once you admit you're powerless, it empowers you. I had an argument with one of the screws in the prison on the Isle of Wight. (Only time I've been off the mainland, and that was in handcuffs.) I came out the cell and this guy's always picking on me and I said, "D'you know, guv, I'm a free man." He said,

'"How d'you work that out, then? Look around you!"

'I said, "I'm a free man, and I'll prove it. Look, I follow the rules here. I made the choice to follow your rules." It's the same with addiction; once you realise that you're powerless, that realisation is empowering because now you see it as a problem to be worked on. Once you accept the situation you're in, you can start doing something about it. And that applies to being homeless. I think that's why I liked it so much, because I had a very big garden. And when people used to say, "Move!" I'd say, "Get off me; you're in *my* garden!" And it also changed me because it took something from me; it took my sense of embarrassment, which I don't want back. The average person has a sense of embarrassment. For example, I dunno, you fart in public. That doesn't bother me. Homelessness changes you. There's no way back.'

Araminta can't imagine a life without embarrassment.

'Then I was kidnapped!'

'What on earth?'

'Yeah', Jed laughs. 'There was this woman I knew from when I'd been homeless under the bandstand in Eastbourne; total pain in the arse. She came to Tunbridge Wells, where I was doing a bit of busking in the precinct, and she got the hump because I was getting money and she wasn't. She got me arrested. I hadn't had a drink that day, I was getting the shakes, retching, the sweats, all that, and the police took me to Pembury Hospital. The hospital said, "We're admitting you, mate!" So they detoxed me. Now, I was s'posed to go to probation during that, so the nurse phoned probation to tell them I wasn't *not* going; I was in hospital. Anyway, I'm coming out of hospital, just getting my discharge letter, and this guy walks up to me and says, "Hello, I'm your driver." I had no idea who he was, so I said, "It's alright, mate, I'll walk." I was gonna do some begging on the way back. He was pretty insistent, so I thought, "Oh, alright, I'll get a lift back, then." When we reached the turning to Tunbridge Wells from Pembury, and he didn't take it, I said, "Hang on mate, I grew up round here, it's that way!" He just ignored me. I got annoyed then, and I said, "Right, I'm not having this. Pull over, and if you don't, I'll pull you over!" He didn't. So I grabbed the steering wheel; gear stick in neutral, pulled it over for him. And he reached over and said, "Read that." A letter. I tore open the envelope and read it. We weren't going to Tunbridge Wells; we were going to Loughborough; two hundred miles away. What had happened was when the nurse had phoned probation, they asked, "Are you detoxing him?" She said, "Yes, we've got to; that's what he's in for." So Probation said, "We've got a rehab for him to go to; it's in Leicestershire." The letter stipulated that if I didn't go to this rehab, I'd be in breach of probation and taken back to court. So I had to go.

'It was a full-on, heavyweight Christian rehab. No therapy; they wanted to pray it out of you. Guess what it was called? The Carpenter's Arms. Seriously. And opposite was an off licence. It's gets weirder and weirder.

Everybody knows I like singing. At The Carpenter's Arms, I wasn't allowed to sing anything but Christian songs. I'm a folk singer, for God's sake. I sing in car parks and places like that; anywhere there's an echo. I was singing in the kitchen; Bad Moon Rising, Creedence Clearwater Revival. They said that if I didn't stop singing, I'd have to leave. I told them where to go.

'Meanwhile, a year and a half beforehand I had to go for an ESA (Employment and Support Allowance) medical work capability assessment, and they kicked me off my benefit. So I appealed it. The appeal went on for eighteen months. The way the rehab was funded, they took all your benefit income, and you were allowed to keep ten pounds for toiletries. You weren't allowed off the premises; you got a shopping list, and you ticked off what you wanted. Prayer sessions during the day and basically a naughty boys' monastery sort of place. In order to sort out their funding, they got on the phone to ESA to say I was in rehab, so the appeal was rushed through, and upheld. The day they kicked me out, I got £9,728. So I've been in hospital, got kidnapped, taken to Leicestershire to a nut-job place, then been booted out with the best part of ten grand, back on the streets. What d'you think happened? An addict with that sort of cash? It was gonna go well, wasn't it? Yeah, I came back to Tunbridge Wells and blew the lot in three months.

'For a while I was living in the car park at the back of the Pantiles; the little one. That was right in front of my front gate; opposite the house where I grew up. That was *my* car park. That was my turf, and everybody bleedin' well knew it as well; still is. I got sunburnt on my head and I ended up going to hospital because it got infected. I got a flesh-eating bug and got quarantined. You can see where the dressing was; that's all scar tissue. They had to detox me while I was in hospital because I was alcohol-dependent, getting the shakes all the time. When I came out, I thought, "Right, I'm not forced to drink now." I wanted to stop drinking. I wondered how I was going to do it. I got up the following morning, out of my sleeping bag. I was with Bilko. He asked, "Where are you off to?" I said, "I've got something I've gotta do; catch you later." I went round every off licence, every pub, all the homeless, all the scallywags, and Chalky, and said to 'em all, "I'm not drinking; I'm detoxed. If you see me drinking, kick shit out of me or get me arrested or something." Everybody seemed to go with it; they were all alright about it. And if there was anybody that had a can, they were like, "Oh sorry, Jed." I did five months on the streets not drinking.

'Then Pauline, the outreach worker from Porchlight, the homelessness charity, heard about it and she got me into the Kenwood Trust in Maidstone. That was how my recovery started. I was with them for a while, but it wasn't a detox; it was supported accommodation. I ended up leaving there for several reasons, but one of them was that I thought I could do more or less on my own what they were offering. The therapy they were offering was Narcotics Anonymous and Change Grow Live, and I could do that in a flat on my own. I'd tried going to AA (Alcoholics Anonymous), but I don't like it; it's too cliquey, too rigid, and inflexible. It's "You're addicted to alcohol – deal with that", but that's not what addiction is. The problem is that you have the *disease* of addiction. Whether I'm addicted to alcohol, cocaine, sex, mobile phones, or remote controls, it's an addiction. For instance, if I give up my mobile phone addiction, it'll end up being a remote control addiction. AA won't deal with that; they think alcohol's the problem. And – especially having studied psychology – I wanted a more therapeutic approach. So I applied to go to Shepherd House, in Maidstone. But then we went into lockdown.'

'Didn't all the homeless get housed in lockdown?'

'Yeah, sort of. They moved me, with all the local homeless, into the *Russell Hotel*. Some of them I hadn't seen before; they weren't from Tunbridge Wells. I don't know who they were, but they were trying to get me to buy them drugs. I was trying to stay clean. We came to blows. I got hold of Chalky and he came round. He said, "I'll have a word with him, but we're releasing people early from prison because of lockdown and trying not to arrest people." So Chalky had a word, but the next day the guy beat me up again. I took my sleeping bag and left. I didn't quite realise what I was letting myself in for. Homelessness in lockdown.

'So I went to Tonbridge, and kipped opposite the police station for a bit, and then got arrested, 'cause I woke up in the morning, and asked a woman the time. She was quite happy, but the police rushed over, and said, "Right, you're nicked for breaking social distancing rules." They kept me in all day and all night. In the morning when they released me, they said, "We've realised we can't do you for social distancing because you're homeless, so we'll do you for drunk and disorderly instead." Which was rubbish because I'd just got out of my sleeping bag, I hadn't had a drink and I'd seen the nurse because I was shaking so badly. I thought, "I'm not having this, I'm going back to bed." I refused to come out of my cell. I went back to sleep, and they crept up, handcuffed me, and put a spit hood over my head. Covid rule. But it was the one and only time I've actually been thrown out of a police station. I don't know anyone else that's happened to.

'Anyway, check this out because my journey through lockdown was nuts! So, I'm handcuffed, with a spit hood over my head, and they take me out the back way. I'm on the corner of a road, and they said, "Right, we're gonna unlock you; put your hands by your sides." So I did. They said, "Take your hood off, put it on the ground. If you look to your right, there's a bag with your property in it and inside that is a travel warrant for anywhere in the South East – get outta town!"

'So I buggered off to London. Feet up in the train in First Class. Get to London, having a fag outside Victoria Station, and – I've got a smoker's cough – I coughed. Two mounted police officers come along. They look down from horseback, and say, "You've got Covid." They marched me, with them on horseback, to St. Thomas's Hospital. I had to walk in front, with them behind me. Traffic queuing up behind us. It was like a scene from *Gladiator*. It's about a mile; took an hour. They took me to casualty, told security not to let me out. I was in there all bleedin' day. Then they said, "There's nothing wrong with you; you can go." Didn't even get tested for Covid.

'So, I spent a few days in London messing about, then I went to Maidstone. Started living in a car park, which felt weird because I'm homeless living in Maidstone with the Kent Covid Variant all around us. At the back of the car park was a hotel where they put all the homeless. It evolved so that we had our own little crew, and the car park was our hangout, as if it was our local pub. It was an abandoned building site; a block of flats where they'd literally just left everything because of Covid, and walked off site. There were all kinds of things there: hand tools, chisels, saws, bricks. The first thing I did was build a brick barbie, went round the shop, and nicked a load of steak.'

'I don't understand how you're able to keep stealing steak from supermarkets like that.'

'It's actually quite easy. You see, while they're looking at me, they're not looking at my hands. All I have to do is keep eye contact and keep them interested in me. I can steal it right in front of them.

'So this car park became a kind of meeting place and none of us were taking notice of any of the rules regarding Covid. How can you when you're homeless? None of us got it, which we should have done, drinking each other's beers, and sharing spliffs. There was no help for the homeless then. The only thing was the Outreach, and they gave you a carrier bag with things like crisps and Mars bars; that was it.

'Then I was given emergency accommodation in a flat above a gift shop. It was only supposed to be for three months, but the Government brought in the policy that under lockdown you can't be evicted, so I was there for fourteen. It was like being homeless, but with a roof. They had odd rules. You weren't allowed to have people staying over; you weren't allowed guests past nine in the evening; you weren't allowed to put up a permanent TV aerial on the building. I was constantly drinking – what else do you do in the middle of lockdown? Then Pauline came round one day with an iPad. She said she'd got an assessment for this detox place. Whole thing took five minutes. They take scallywags here, you see. She said she'd get me a detox, so, seven months ago, Pauline drove me to a detox and that was the last drink I had. Ten days there, then the rest of the time here.'

'And it's good here? You like it?'

'The thing I like here is their commitment to recovery. All the staff are in recovery, too; they come to the meetings with us. So it isn't like in prison, or at school, or with probation, or with the boss at work; there isn't a "them and us". If you break the rules, they're in charge, but there isn't the two-tier system; the hierarchy. It's been a bit of a bumpy ride, but now it *does* feel like home. I *do* want more therapy, but if I leave here now, I wouldn't half miss it. It's 'cause there's no other head like an addict's head. They're my brethren; they're my crew. You can go anywhere in the world to a Fellowship meeting, and you can say certain things, and somebody'll say, "And me; just the same for me." When I went to that flat, it was homelessness with a roof and a cooker. If I'd gone to that flat via this place, I'd probably have been able to deal with it.

'I'll be here anything up to two years. But Mum's getting older and older; dottier and dottier. I'd give it a year before she needs full-time care. My sister's a property developer. She already owns about six houses, and she's thinking of buying one for Mum. So when I leave here, I might move in and stay with Mum until she leaves this mortal coil. I'm not afraid of nursing her through dementia. I grew up with a brain-damaged Mum, and all it is, is a worse version of that. Mum's Mum. She wouldn't be the same if she hadn't had the accident, but I wouldn't change her; I love her to bits. I phone her every day. I've been pushing her around in a wheelchair since I was big enough to push one. Total angel, just never got the chance to shine, 'cause of Dad. If Mum hadn't had her accident, Dad just wouldn't have...

he wasn't on the same level, if you see what I mean. The only reason Dad managed to pull Mum was because she was brain-damaged.

'If being Mum's carer doesn't happen, there's something I want to do. I want to promote using therapy with the Steps. I reckon they'd make a brilliant combination. The therapy system doesn't like the Fellowship and vice versa. It's a pity because they're two sides of the same coin. We could just get them together and make a complete coin.

'It's a bit of a joke here, actually: there's a Fellowship expression, "Keep it simple, stupid; don't overcomplicate it." But it's my nature to overcomplicate things. It's called a "high need for cognition". It's a bit like you're driving along in the car, the accelerator's floored and you're in first gear. You do ten miles an hour with the engine screaming away, and you're not allowed to change up. How d'you save the engine from blowing up? Drive uphill; give it a load; give it work to do. That's what my brain needs. That's one of the reasons why I like altering my perception; to look at the same thing but from different angles.

'In therapy, I've been talking about my dad, who died three months ago. I've got a lot of anger and resentment towards him, but it felt really weird because I didn't feel much when he died. I thought there was something wrong with me. You could call it "dysfunctional grieving", but I find these labels meaningless. The anti-psychiatry movement of the seventies said we react in sane ways to insane situations. From that point of view there's no such thing as insanity. So that label's unhelpful because my grieving's not dysfunctional; it's just different. That's why I think that label of dysfunction's unhelpful. My older brother – I don't care about him, and neither does the rest of my family because he was a real git. Mum often asks me why I don't like him, and I say, "Because any ounce of love I had for him, he beat it out of me." Now, for me, not caring about him; that seems to be quite logical. But other people would say it's dysfunctional.

'One of the things that's come up here – it's quite a battle for me and it's quite tough, physically, spiritually, and emotionally – something I discovered: my core addiction is I'm obsessed with being obsessed. I'm addicted to being addicted. The philosopher, Hegel, said you can't know what something is until you know what it isn't. That translates to modern research methodology. You never try and prove a hypothesis right; you only try and prove it wrong. The longer you can't, the more likely it is to be true. What goes up must come down used to be true, but it isn't now, because now we've got space travel. So you try and destroy a theory. The more you can't, the better a theory it is. I think that's very much like my thinking; trying to find out what's real and what isn't; what's reality. In a sense, the quest for the soul.

'At least all this thinking keeps me guessing; keeps my mind busy if nothing else. Thinking about the future, if you ask me to predict what will happen to me, I have to say I just don't know. I don't know where I'm going, or what I'm doing. All I can say at the moment is right now, I'm sober. I'm clean. Just for today.'

***

As Araminta walks back up the hill to her house, she feels exhausted by Jed's story; the insistent energy that runs through everything he says, which must be that need of his to always be in first gear, going uphill. She thinks about entrenched homelessness: living on the streets feeling you have everything you need provided for you by charity shops, shoplifted steaks, and electricity wired from lamp posts. She wonders what it must be like to be completely lawless. Not immoral, exactly, but with Jed's philosophy of life that allowed him to storm out of the castle the rest of us live in, and as he left, catapult embarrassment back over the ramparts.

It occurs to Araminta that everyone she meets is giving her a gift. Jed has shown her it's possible to be free of embarrassment, or, at least to ignore it and not let it in when it comes knocking. Ben has taught her it truly *is* possible to change, and for the better. Denise has reminded her that The Royals are just as vulnerable as anyone else; just as prone to suffer addiction, for example. And Princess Margaret must have been lonely, too. Being royal doesn't mean you're happy. That is so very obvious. So why has she spent a lifetime trying to be posh; her hobby a study of The Royal Family? Maybe it isn't a hobby; maybe it's an obsession.

The Best Laid Plans

Fourteen weeks before the party

At 3.00 on a Saturday afternoon in Secret Street, Aslan reaches over Toby's shoulder to ring No. 11's doorbell, then visibly jumps as a Westminster chime clangs from the doorbell's hanging metal tubes in the hallway. The two men glance at each other and giggle.

The front door swings open to a beaming Araminta.

'Do come inside! Lovely to see you.'

'It was a bit steep', says Toby. 'Aslan met me on the bend and helped me up.'

Aslan's looking down at the wheels of Toby's chair. 'The step's a bit...'

'You tilt me back, then push the back wheel right up to it, then...' Aslan tilts the chair back a little too far, and Toby lurches backwards, 'Whoa!'

'Sorry, so sorry', says Aslan.

'It's fine, it tips up easily; it's a sort of sports wheelchair', says Toby.

Aslan rights the chair, and hoiks Toby up and into the hallway.

'I have it balanced so it goes as fast as possible', says Toby, 'although, there isn't usually anywhere to...' A Staffordshire bull terrier's grinning head appears at his side. 'Oh, hello', says Toby, and gives the dog a pat on the head. 'Lovely colour – that grey he is.'

'It's "blue", but that's just breeders' snobbery; it's grey, really.' At the other end of the lead is the smiling woman in the green duffle coat that Araminta sees walking the dog in the mornings. She has an Irish accent. 'Sorry, I had to bring Wilf. Is that alright? I can't leave him; he whines when he's alone. Pete's gone to watch the rugby and the kids are meeting their mates down by the clock tower. Sorry, I'm Aoife; I should have said. I brought his blanket; he'll sit quietly on that.'

Wilf grins up at Araminta.

'Oh, that's fine, we like dogs', says Araminta.

Aoife wonders whether that's the royal "we".

Araminta beckons them in, 'Come through, come through into the living room...'

Sitting smugly within the horseshoe of three vast yellow damask Knowle sofas, the polished walnut coffee table is laid out with blue and white peacock-patterned China cups and saucers, matching milk jug, sugar bowl with sugar cubes, silver tongs, and side plates. There are larger plates of circular pastries with strawberry jam in the middle, and petticoat tail shortbread.

'Oh, God, your rug!' says Toby, 'My wheels are...'

'It's fine', says Araminta, 'a Persian silk rug is surprisingly forgiving. And it's lovely that you're here. Look, I've made you a space next to Beatrice and Nancy. Aslan, you can sit here, the other side of Toby. Aoife, you sit next to Aslan'.

Toby wheels himself where Araminta gestures, next to one of the high-sided sofas. He puts on his brakes, and peeps over the sofa side at Beatrice, who smiles back at him.

Nancy cranes her neck past Beatrice to give Toby a wry little smile and a wave. Aoife arranges Wilf's tartan blanket on the floor next to her feet, and sits beside Aslan on the sofa next to Beatrice and Nancy. The doorbell chimes again, making Aslan jump once again, then chuckle along with Toby. Araminta opens the door to find Jed standing there, with his politest smile plastered all over his weather-beaten face. 'Is it alright? You know, how I said the therapists want us to be more involved with the local community.'

'Oh, how lovely, yes, of course, I hoped you'd come.'

Araminta accompanies him to the front room and announces, 'This is Jed, everybody'.

Jed looks for a spare seat, to find the only one is facing Toby. He'd been hoping Toby – or "Chalky", to Jed – wouldn't be there. He thinks of all the times the police have moved him on, hassled him, arrested him for nothing; just for existing, but he's hesitated for too long, and has to sit down quickly now, or people will think him weird. He knows they already have their opinions about him. Toby's thinking about the run-ins he's had with Jed, how Jed was lairy when he was drunk, how he hassled passers-by, his breath stinking of booze, the smell of it ingrained in his flesh. But Jed is in recovery now, and Toby retired. Toby decides he must give Jed a chance. With a gentle smile, he regards him, and thinks he detects a quietness in him that he hasn't seen in the past. They give each other an almost undiscernible nod.

Araminta marches briskly to the kitchen and returns with two teapots on a silver tray. 'The Burleigh Blue Peacock teapot's Assam; the gold and white Victoria and Albert teapot is from the Royal Collection shop – I couldn't resist it. There's Earl Grey in that one. Twining's, of course.'

'Of course!' grins Toby.

'The Burleigh was one of Queen Mary's favourites', says Araminta, 'and look, as well as Her Majesty's favourite tea, we have her favourite pastries: jam pennies! Do help yourselves. There are all-butter petticoat tails if you prefer; they were my dear departed Frederick's favourites'.

Araminta begins pouring tea and handing it round. 'Assam? Oh, lovely, you're joining me in Earl Grey, Jed.'

Teacups rattle in saucers. Toby balances a plate with a shortbread slice and a jam penny on his knees, and slurps his tea, loudly. Aoife smiles at Aslan as he struggles to fit his large fingers comfortably through the dainty handle, gives up, and picks up the teacup with his hands either side, as if it's a bowl. Araminta hands him a saucer, which he obediently puts beneath his cup.

Jed picks out three sugar cubes one by one with the silver tongs and plops them into his cup. 'They have these cubes at the Mount Pleasant caff', he says.

Araminta looks a little cross. The Mount Pleasant Café is anything but pleasant, as far as she's concerned; a greasy spoon with sticky brown and red sauce bottles on the Formica tables, and discount dinners for pensioners. Araminta doesn't consider herself a pensioner, not in that sense – the impoverished sense.

'They do a very good full English breakfast in there', says Beatrice.

Araminta can't hide her surprise. Beatrice tucking into egg, bacon, sausage, beans, and fried bread in the Mount Pleasant Café? It isn't easy to imagine. She quickly brings her attention back to the small stack of A4 paper on her lap. 'I've typed an agenda, so we don't forget anything', she says.

'Right, yes, good idea', says Nancy, trying to join in with Araminta's enthusiasm.

'Pass them round, pass them round...' says Araminta. The agenda is printed on the same watermarked white paper with the crown emblem as her invitation letters. 'Before we look at the agenda, I want to share my vision for the party with you, and then we can discuss it. How would that be?'

The room is silent.

Unnerved, Araminta continues, 'Well, I'd like it to be a chic event, as is fitting for a royal celebration. I propose to hire gazebos in case of rain, trestle tables, so that they all fit together in one smooth long rectangle, and nice white damask table cloths, just like the ones they have at royal banquets. Well, not quite like that, because they won't be embroidered with royal crests, of course, but in keeping, you see?'

No one says a word.

'And I thought it would be lovely to have matching napkins, with silver napkin rings. Then I thought we should all have a buttonhole, perhaps with a spray of lily of the valley – they're Her Majesty's favourite; she had them in her coronation bouquet – and then fresh flowers for table decorations. Something red, white, and blue, or purple.'

Araminta stops to catch her breath, and looks around the room hoping for enthusiastic faces, but the others are slightly fazed, and working out what to say.

Wilf stands up, turns around and flops down again on his blanket. His bowels choose that moment to perforate the silence with a tiny balloon-squeak of a fart. Aoife's cheeks turn slightly red. The others stifle chuckles, then their noses begin to wrinkle and their mouths twist into a disgusted grimace as an unmistakable eggy stench creeps around the room and reaches their nostrils. Aoife's cheeks turn from rose to burgundy, and she blurts out, 'I'm so sorry, it's his age', at the same time realising the full horror of what she's said, as she looks over to eighty-two-year-old Araminta.

Araminta pretends she's oblivious.

To rescue Aoife, Jed says, 'This is all very lovely, Ara...'

'Araminta.'

'Araminta, but it's gonna cost a bloody fortune!'

'Oh, don't worry about that; I have funds to cover it. It will be my treat for the street.' Araminta's delighted at her little rhyme.

'That's very generous of you', says Aslan, 'but are you sure it's necessary?'

'Well, we don't want a scruffy, ramshackle affair, do we? Not in Royal Tunbridge Wells.'

'You can't guarantee that some of the silver napkin rings won't go astray', says Toby.

'Oh *do* let me, it's such an historic occasion. Let me treat you all!'

Jed sighs, thinking how much it will cost, and wondering how many rental deposits you could buy with the money. Then to stop himself appearing grouchy he says, 'I'll help with the tables; you know, putting them out and everything'.

Assuming everyone's vision for the party is now the same as hers, Araminta continues, 'Item one: road closure. We'll need to apply to the council'.

'I'll do that', says Toby, helpfully.

'That would be lovely, Toby, thank you. We have plenty of time, but I suppose the sooner the better. You can do it online via the council's website.'

'I'll get to it when I get home.'

'Oh, and I meant to say, before, that I would also like to supply bunting. I've seen delightful hand-sewn cotton Union Jack bunting in Closs & Hamblin on Mount Pleasant.'

'But I was going to offer to organise the kids in the street to make some with potato prints', says Aoife.

Araminta remembers art lessons at primary school: sugar paper with cotton wool stuck on for clouds, and tatty Mothering Sunday cards sent home with squiffy painted daffodils and boss-eyed bunnies. 'Oh, let me buy the cotton ones. Perhaps we can re-use them for Her Majesty's next anniversary. The next item is food.'

'Well, that's easy', says Aoife, 'people can bring their own'.

Araminta looks dubious. 'What if they bring the wrong sort of thing?'

'What would be the wrong sort of thing?' says Aoife.

'Like shop-bought cakes, for instance, instead of nice home-baked ones', says Araminta.

'What's wrong with shop-bought cakes?' asks Aslan. 'I like Mr Kipling cakes – mini Battenbergs are addictive.'

'Viennese whirls are better', says Toby.

'How can you say a Viennese whirl is better than a mini Battenberg?' says Aslan.

'No one likes marzipan!' says Toby.

'Of course they do! It's in Christmas cakes and wedding cakes, isn't it?' says Jed.

'Yes, but no one actually enjoys marzipan, though, do they?' replies Toby.

'Well, I do', says Aslan, 'and Viennese whirls are so crumbly that most of it ends up on the plate'.

'Not if you stuff it in all in one', says Toby.

'I like Fondant Fancies', says Beatrice. 'When Hugo was little, he used to call them Fandant Foncies'.

Nancy sits silently, sipping her black tea, as unwanted memories flit into her mind of her reluctant walks to the corner shop; her mother's anxious face each time Nancy returned with Fondant Fancies.

'The pink and yellow ones, though, not the brown ones', adds Aslan, thoughtfully.

Nancy shakes herself out of the memory. 'I'll have Platinum Jubilee cup cakes made specially, at the patisserie', she says.

'You know, I admit now that when you arrived, I was hoping you might say something like that. Your cakes are divine!' says Araminta.

Nancy smiles.

'I love your strawberry cup cakes with the buttercream icing, and the little strawberry pieces on top', says Beatrice.

'They're very popular', says Nancy.

'I don't know how you stay so slim', says Beatrice, 'making all those sumptuous cakes. I'd be twenty stone if I ran that patisserie'.

Nancy tries to muster a smile, hoping it doesn't look anything like the anger she really wants to express. She wants to shout, 'Shut up! Leave me alone!' What would people think if they really knew she had never eaten any of her famous Pantiles Patisserie strawberry cupcakes?

Jed doesn't understand it, but notices her discomfort, and changes the subject. 'Will there be alcohol?' he says.

'Item three: drinks', says Araminta, approvingly.

'Because I'm not sure the others at the recovery house will want to come if there's alcohol.'

'Oh dear! I was going to order cases of English sparkling wine from Biddenden Vineyard.'

'I would love it if alcohol didn't exist', says Beatrice. 'Some people get in such a pickle with it.' She finds herself looking at Jed. 'Sorry, Jed, you know what I...'

'I know *exactly* what you mean!'

Beatrice smiles. 'It's a lunchtime thing, isn't it? So people don't need to drink alcohol, do they?'

'I suppose it would be safer if no one's drinking; it can bring out the worst in some people', says Toby, as images of late-night brawls outside Sticky's Nightclub spring into his mind.

'Surely people will bring their own drinks?' says Aoife.

'Perhaps we should specify no alcohol?' suggests Toby.

'How about sparkling cordials?' says Araminta, 'Elderflower, maybe?'

'Oo, I like elderflower!' says Beatrice.

'I prefer Coke', says Toby.

'Lemonade is maybe more English', Aslan suggests.

'But everyone likes Coke', says Toby, 'or maybe...'

'Let's think about drinks later and move on', says Araminta, interrupting.

They refer back to their agendas. Toby's has slid onto the floor. Aslan picks it up and gives it to him with a wink and a smile, whispering, 'This is serious!'

Toby snorts another giggle, rattling his teacup.

Araminta ignores them. 'Music. I was thinking brass band music, you know, as they have in the Changing of the Guard. Something regal. I Vow to Thee, My Country; that sort of thing.'

'Why don't we get the Sally Army?' says Toby, 'They could march up and down the street with their trombones, and bang their big bass drum'.

'Why not the massed bands of the Royal Marines?' says Jed, winking.

Aoife, Beatrice, and Toby burst out laughing.

'Stephen can't abide the Salvation Army', says Nancy. The laughter abates a little. 'They wanted to come in the pub at Christmas and play a carol and have a collection, and he ordered them out. Quite rudely.'

'Is it religion? Does he have a thing about religion?' says Aslan. 'Because people can be very funny about religion, you know, it can be a sort of political thing.'

'It must be hard being a Muslim in a Christian country', says Beatrice.

'I'm not a Muslim! Just because I have light brown skin and a beard doesn't mean I'm a Muslim. Lara and I go to All Saints every Sunday morning.'

'Oh, I'm so sorry, I should never have assumed.' Beatrice looks shamefaced.

'It's alright. As long as you don't think I'm a terrorist.'

'That's just bloody stupid, for anyone to think that', says Jed.

Beatrice still feels embarrassed. 'No, of course...'

'Someone put this comment on the accountancy practice's Google review', says Aslan. '*When I saw Mr Hossein, I was afraid he might be wearing a suicide belt beneath his suit, but he was actually very nice.*'

'No!' says Araminta, wide-eyed.

'Yep.' Aslan looks down at the yellow silk rug.

'It's awful you have to deal with this sort of nonsense', says Aoife. Then after a suitable pause, continues, 'Talking of things we have to deal with, we must consider safeguarding issues'.

'Must we?' asks Araminta, wishing she'd thought to put it on the agenda.

'That's a tad OTT, isn't it?' asks Beatrice.

'Unfortunately, no, it isn't', says Aoife.

'I'm sure there's no one in Secret Street who's been engaged in any sort of...' Araminta struggles to find an acceptable word, '...criminal activity?'

Toby immediately thinks of three, but keeps schtum.

'The important thing is', says Aoife, 'for everyone to keep an eye on their own children and know where they are at all times. It's all too easy at these events for parents and guardians to assume that everyone's safe with children, but they might not be'.

'I think we're going to need another letter', says Toby, 'advising people to watch their children; tell them what is and isn't provided; confirm the date and timings...'

'...and of course, item five: parking', says Araminta.

'Oh dear, people aren't going to like that', says Beatrice, 'there's never anywhere to park as it is'.

'I'm sure, for this special occasion, people will be happy to park around the corner. There will be plenty of room because it's a bank holiday, so there won't be any commuters parked there', says Araminta, pleased with herself for thinking this all through before the meeting. She'd had a chat with Arthur next door, too, and he'd been helpful on legal, municipal bits and pieces. 'And the cars will only have to remain there until the tables are put away.' (Araminta was also pleased with herself for using the word "remain"; it was posher than "stay". She'd learned that from an episode of *Morse*.) 'It will only be for a few hours. How about I write a letter, and then maybe a couple of you could come back again, and we'll plan what to...'

She's interrupted by the chiming doorbell.

Aslan jumps out of his skin, and his dainty teacup and saucer topple from his lap. He watches, horrified, as the saucer lands on its side and rolls, as if in slow motion, across the carpet, before coming to rest beneath the table, while the tea seeps into the yellow rug in front of him. 'Oh, no! I'm so sorry, I'm so sorry...' He jumps up with his hands over his face, watching through his fingers as the brown puddle seeps deeper and wider into the silky yellow pile. He begins to quiver. For a moment, the others can't help staring at him.

Araminta says, cheerily, 'That will come up in a jiffy! Nancy, sweetie, could you pop in the kitchen and fetch the kitchen roll to mop it up a bit, while I see to the door?' Araminta smiles at Aslan, and goes to answer the door. She opens it to find Councillor Petty in his signature Panama hat, a tight-fitting grey suit, and white shirt with a regimental striped tie.

'I'm sorry I'm late; I was held up on very important Council business', he says.

'Sorry, I don't understand; late?'

'For your street party planning meeting.'

'Oh! Well, yes, but only people who live in Secret Street were invited.'

'It's in my ward, of course...'

'But you don't live in the street.'

'Everything that happens in Lansdowne Ward is my concern.'

'Well, we've nearly finished now, so there's no point in you...'

'You may not know, not having the experience of these sorts of things as I do, that you will need to apply for planning permission.'

'We don't need planning perm...'

'...and of course you must apply to Kent Highways for road closure', says Councillor Petty, butting in.

'You don't need to; it's a specific council thing; they do it all for...'

'You must also consider parking issues. A letter will need...'

'It's all in hand, Councillor Petty. Now I have a rug to attend to.'

The mention of the rug confuses Councillor Petty and momentarily stops him midflow.

'Goodbye', says Araminta, firmly, and closes the door in front of his pointed nose. She walks back into the living room. 'It was that wretched little mansplaining man', she announces, 'Councillor Petty, trying to tell me things I already know'.

'Oo, well', says Beatrice, 'You know he took the credit for getting that new community centre built in the park, to replace the old ramshackle heap of a hut that was there before? Well, it wasn't down to him at all!'

'Oh?' says Nancy, still on her knees on the rug with Aslan, where they're working their way through a roll of jubilee crown-embossed kitchen roll, patting it onto the rug to soak up the tea.

'No, it was the council planning department, reminding the developers who built that executive home development of their legal responsibilities!'

'Chatsworth Heights?' says Araminta.

'That's the one. They had to provide facilities as a condition of their planning permission', says Beatrice.

'I'm sure I saw him on Facebook, crowing about that', says Nancy, 'with a photo of him grinning in front of it'.

'You would have', says Araminta. 'My dear departed Frederick used to call his sort "Captain Mainwarings". You know; that pompous twit on *Dad's Army*? One hundred per cent confidence in his own ability, but no actual ability'.

The others laugh, but Aslan is still shaking.

'See?' says Aoife, nudging Aslan, 'It's going to be fine'.

'I will have the rug dry-cleaned', says Aslan.

'No need, I have a marvellous rose-scented Stainaway Spray', replies Araminta, breezily.

'Sorry', says Aoife, 'it's only just sunk in; Councillor Petty took the credit for the community centre, but it was actually the council that organised it?'

'Yep!' says Araminta.

'Atrocious behaviour!' says Beatrice.

'Desperate for votes', says Toby, shaking his head in disapproval.

Beatrice and Jed stand up to leave.

'Thank you so much for having us', says Beatrice.

'Let's a few of us meet again', says Araminta, as she heads to the kitchen for her dish cloth and carpet spray, calling out, 'I'll sort the letters. I can chivvy the people who haven't replied yet, so we have a better idea of numbers'.

Toby unclamps his brakes and manoeuvres out to the hallway. 'Come on Aslan, you can give me a hand down the step.' Aslan reluctantly stops mopping the rug, and thanks Nancy. Aoife's picking up Wilf's blanket and folding it.

As the last of them leave, Araminta waves them off with her dish cloth. 'Thank you all so much for coming, it's been marvellous!' She closes the front door behind them, returns to the remnant of the tea puddle that the kitchen roll mopping has left behind, and gleefully gives it a rose-scented squirt. She imagines Secret Street with the white damask tablecloths, silver napkin rings, smart gazebos, and jubilee-themed cup cakes. She thinks of everyone wearing her lily of the valley button holes, knowing who she is, feeling grateful to her, raising their champagne flutes high to toast her. She imagines a celebratory chorus of, 'To Araminta!', and how she'll blush and fluster as they sip their sparkling drinks, the bubbles rising with the joy in her heart.

98A Secret Street – PC Toby "Chalky" White

Thirteen weeks before the Platinum Jubilee party

Araminta feels pleased with herself. She's getting rather good at this. She's started going to the pub, taking a book, in case there's no one to talk to, but with the aim of getting to chat with neighbours. It's about six o'clock, and the only other customers are a man sitting on a stool at the bar reading *The Kent Bugle*, and a couple on the red button-back sofa in the opposite corner. Then Toby from No. 98 comes in. He can access The Otter in his wheelchair through the car park and the back door, but to order a drink, he has to look up at the bar from his seated position, and Araminta thinks that makes him look like Oliver Twist asking for more gruel, and offers to buy him a pint, if he feels like chatting. She carries their drinks to a corner table where there's room for Toby's wheelchair, and as she sits down beside him, she asks how he came to be a policeman.

'I only applied for a joke', he says. 'I saw the ad in the paper, and said to my wife, Hilary – then my girlfriend – that I would apply. She thought it was hysterical because I was really anti-establishment; into all that left wing hippy stuff. This was the mid-eighties. I worked for CND as a volunteer and helped steward their marches in London. I went on marches for the miners and also did fundraising for them during the miners' strike.'

'It's hard to believe you were a policeman, hearing this, and looking at you now', Araminta says.

Toby has a small, plain steel earring in his left ear, long, wavy brown hair, and is wearing black jeans and a grey jumper worn thin at the elbows. 'Yeah', he says, 'I went on anti-Thatcher demos. The marches attracted over a hundred thousand people, and there were often clashes with the police. I thought my CND work would flash up with the police on some list or another, or indeed my presence on the demos, because my comrades and I assumed everyone was being tracked'.

'They weren't, though?'

'No. The other thing was you had to be fit to join the police, and I wasn't at the time. Running had always been my thing; the thing I was good at. My parents rather pointlessly sent me to a private school – I only came out with CSE Maths and O Level English – but the school found out I could run, and I soon became a county champion of the fifteen hundred metres, and captain of the cross-country team. I used to run fifty miles a week and do races and events and athletics.'

'Oh, no, you must miss it so much!'

'I do. Then I went to drama college, and took up smoking, and used to smoke dope as well.'

'You must be the world's most unlikely police recruit', she says.

Toby nods. 'The whole thing was bluff. In fact, I caused great hilarity with one of the superintendents because one of the first things they asked was "How did you get here today?" and I said, "I hitched a lift." I also wore an orange cable-knit jumper, which amused them; they thought this jumper was inappropriate. They said in the invitation it was a two-day assessment and you needed to wear a tie and so on for the second day with the formal interview, so my assumption was that therefore you could just wear what you liked on the first day. Everyone else turned up quite smart with collar and tie, and I was just wearing jeans, a t-shirt, and that jumper. I'd just had a haircut, but my hair was still quite long. The superintendent said, "Why haven't you had a haircut?" I said, "I had one yesterday." The superintendent replied, "You're joking!"

Araminta smiles.

'So, the assessment was things like being able to argue, public speaking, written tests, maths and writing, a group discussion, and a teamwork exercise. At the end of that first day the superintendent sat me down and asked why I wanted to join the police. I'd had run-ins with them in the past and I was unhappy about the way I'd been treated. Stop and search in London. I was going to a drama class, wearing an army surplus greatcoat, and I had a bag on my shoulder. They said, "You resemble a description of a suspect for a burglary that's just happened. We're going to search your bag." They backed me into a doorway and stood over me. I'm five feet nine inches tall. In those days, all policemen had to be six feet tall as an entry requirement, and they were wearing their helmets, too. I was frightened, and indignant, knowing they were simply doing it because I had long hair, and because they could. So, I believed that I had something to offer; that I came from a different background to the norm. I thought I could improve the police force and serve the community. Throughout the entire assessment day I was roundly mocked for having gone to drama school, and I just kept brushing it off and saying that it was useful because it was about listening to people and understanding people's emotions.

'At the end of the day was an interview with the superintendent, who said my background was a useless, morally suspect, chancing layabout lifestyle. I was twenty-eight, living hand-to-mouth doing odd jobs, cash-in-hand work, signing on. I'd just finished working for a language school, looking after foreign students over the summer, and the only job I could get was working for a mechanic, sandblasting old equipment before selling it on. The superintendent was deliberately trying to antagonise me. I remained calm. At the end of the day, a few people were sent home. But I was still there.

'That evening there were drinks in the bar, and we knew we were being watched, so didn't down loads of pints. Everyone went meekly off to bed at nine o'clock. The next day, we were interviewed by a panel of three: an assistant chief constable, a Police Federation rep, who was from Yorkshire, and the superintendent. Everyone else was in for twenty minutes and I was in for forty-five. There were all the usual questions denigrating my past experiences. Then they said, "Why did you only apply for Kent Police and no other police forces?" I said that I thought applying for more than one would indicate a lack of faith in my home police force. Apparently, others were applying all over the place. The fed rep said, "Why didn't you apply for Yorkshire?" I said, "Well, I come from Tunbridge Wells – I've got a posh Southern accent – I'm not sure I'd fit in up there." The Yorkshire fed rep took great offence at this.'

'Oh, that's really interesting', says Araminta, 'because I once went on a teaching conference in Yorkshire and there was a local woman there who thought I sounded posh, and therefore assumed I looked down on her. She was really nasty to me, you know, snapped at me in the breakout groups. Nothing I could do about it. Anyway, you obviously got the job...'

'Yes. When I was told I was going to be recruited, the assistant chief constable gave his congratulations and said, "Oh, by the way, do you play rugby?" I ended up playing for Kent Police rugby team for years. Until the accident, of course.

'We were sent to a training college in Ashford where we were in barracks for fourteen weeks and did lots of old-fashioned marching. It was supposed to be character-building. I was always the one who was out of step.' Toby giggled. 'Every day I kept thinking it was soon going to end; they were going to see through me.' He drained his pint.

Araminta had finished her half.

'Another?' Toby asks.

'Yes, please.' Since her new mission to find friends had led her to try the pub, Araminta had discovered she liked real ale. 'Five Points, please, but just a half.' Toby undoes his wheelchair brakes and starts to wheel towards the bar, but Stephen, who's serving, notices him.

'Same again, Toby? I'll bring them over.'

Toby nods and takes out his wallet. Stephen brings the drinks, takes Toby's bank card to the machine behind the bar to pay, brings the card back, then returns to the bar. Araminta involuntarily sighs.

'What?' asks Toby.

'Sorry, I was just thinking it must be hard for you, having to rely on other people.'

'You get used to it; you have to.'

'So what next? What happened when you started work? Any memorable arrests?'

'Oh, God, yes, embarrassing... My first arrest, I was with my tutor – an experienced PC – and we were called to Marks and Spencer where two young mothers, both with babies, had been stuffing baby clothes into the bottom of their buggies. I had to interview each of them in turn. It dawned on me that I'd never done this before, and I didn't know what questions to ask. My colleague had to whisper prompts to me: "Did you pay for these goods?" "How well did you know this person?" "Did this person tell you to do this?" I lamely repeated what he said: "Sorry, yes, did you pay for these goods?" "How well do you know this person?" It was embarrassing. But that wasn't the worst of it. I thought I'd joined the police to help people. My instinct when coming across a woman with a baby in a buggy was to open the door for her, or help her up steps. Here I was arresting a woman with a baby for the theft of clothes. It ended up with me charging both of them. It was their first offence. At one point I was holding a baby and reading the charge sheet at the same time.'

'A conflict of emotions?'

'Yes, you could call it that. During my first two years as PC White – nicknamed "Chalky" by my colleagues, of course – I slowly but surely locked away my compassion and turned into a machine. I didn't know how else to cope with it. I was dealing with violence, unpleasantness, death. Hils found me difficult to live with, and I could understand why. There's a tendency in policing to talk like a police statement instead of a person. So when a normal person would simply say, "walking along", a police officer might say, "proceeding in a northerly direction." It's a daft habit you get stuck in.'

'You still talk a bit like that now, I think, if it's OK to say that?'

'Maybe I do. Some police marriages fail because of it – the lack of emotion.' He takes a sip of his pint. 'No, it's not a lack of emotion; it's a lack of *showing* emotion. Hils was a saint to stick by me. Having said that, Hils is a nurse, and there's a reason nurses, police officers, and firefighters tend to get together.'

'The shifts, you mean?'

'That plays a part, but what I was going to say is, it's more the understanding of what it's like to be dealing with crisis, injury, death, on a daily basis.'

'Oh. Yes, of course.' Araminta feels a fool having offered the wrong explanation. This business of making friends is fraught with difficulty. She looks down into her beer.

'The other thing about being a police officer is that you can be told to do things and there isn't any doubt or question about doing them. Usually there was no point in questioning because there was a perfectly good reason for telling you to do it. Often long, boring shifts, like when we had to come over to Tunbridge Wells (Hils and I didn't live here then) when Princess Diana opened the shopping centre, just to be a police presence.'

'Oh!' Araminta's eyes light up. 'I loved Princess Diana! Tell me all about it!'

'Well, let me think... It was strange when we saw her, in her blue suit, doing that thing of peeping out from beneath her fringe. We may have imagined it, but we thought we could tell she wasn't really happy. It feels odd to be guarding someone when, at the end of the day, they're no different to you.'

Araminta thinks back to her conversation with Denise and decides it's time she begins to get used to this idea that the Royals are no different to anyone else.

'The night before', Toby continues, 'we had to check the area for anything or anyone who might cause a problem for the royal visit; interrupt the event. There were five homeless people that used to hang around there and beg. Pre-police, I might have bunged them a quid. But our instruction was to get rid of them; move them away. We marched up to them and said, "Clear off." We had no authority to do it. Four of them did, but one of them, Jed, thought he'd argue, so they said if he didn't move on he'd get arrested'.

'I know Jed!'

'From the rehab?'

'Yes. "The Recovery House", they call it.'

'A more positive spin. We didn't need to cuff him; he came quietly, and we put him in the van, took him back to Maidstone, gave him dinner, and locked him in the cell for the night. Then in the morning, he was marched straight past the custody desk – no paperwork at all – and out of the back door. There's no record of it, of course.'

'The worst bit of the job, though, was morgue duty.'

'Sorry?'

'The morgue, you know. At Maidstone, which had a main hospital, after five o'clock the morgue was shut, and any bodies coming in – sudden deaths, or whatever – that needed to have an autopsy, we had to go to the main desk, pick up the keys to the mortuary, go down and let the undertaker or whoever it was – usually the undertaker – let them in. This was the shittiest job in the station, so being new, I had to do it a lot. I had to look and check that what was in the black plastic body bag was actually a body, fill in forms, and tie a tag on the toe – all of that. Some of them were truly tragic. A woman who choked to death on a bit of meat and her husband didn't know what to do. She still had her pink socks on. There was a young woman who was going to university and breaking up with her boyfriend. They'd been a couple for years, and he was going to be left behind, so he waited until she was in bed, and climbed up into a tree that grew outside her bedroom and hanged himself, so that it was the first thing she saw in the morning. He was a terribly good-looking guy.'

'Horrendous!'

'Also horrible, but in a different way, was the time they used me as bait.'

'Bait?'

'Yes. I was new and young, and shocked when they told me what I was going to be doing. I didn't feel I could say no. Well, I couldn't. People had been complaining about men hanging around the public toilets at various times of the day; usually in the evening.'

Araminta puts her hand over her mouth and, for a moment, holds her breath.

'It was decided that a squad would be set up to establish how prevalent this was. It involved two other officers, a sergeant, and me. We were all in our twenties, in plain clothes; tight-fitting t-shirts and jeans. One of us would go into the toilets, where you could see phone numbers had been written on the backs of doors, and holes had been drilled through the sides of the booths – "glory holes". I had to have it explained to me what the offenders used to stick through them.'

Araminta goes cold. The dark wood panelled walls of the pub seem to start pressing in on her, preventing her from breathing.

'The officer would wait in a booth with a door shut. Other times we would see someone go in, because they would have clocked the squad, lurking, and the deal was the suspect would go in hoping someone was going to follow him. The policeman would follow them in, and go, not to a urinal, but a booth. The suspect would be standing at the urinal, and they would then go into the booth next to the policeman who would wait for a signal – a knock, or a foot tap – something that would indicate they were not...' Toby draws invisible quotation marks in the air with his fingers "...using the building for the purpose for which it was designed."'

Toby grins, but Araminta doesn't.

'It's from an Alan Bennett sketch', he says.

Araminta smiles, feebly.

'Our squad never gave encouragement', Toby continues, 'because that would be provocation. We did this for about two weeks. I hated it. I was nervous about getting it wrong; anxious with the anticipation I felt in the lengthy periods of waiting for something to happen. But above all, I was angry. Angry to be made to do something that harasses people unfairly and unjustly, sometimes wrecking a marriage for no good reason'.

Araminta doesn't know what to do with herself. She tries to think of a plausible reason to change the subject, but her brain won't let her think clearly. All she can think of is Fred in the toilets at Matfield car park. Fred on that evening when he'd been brought home in a police car, and broken her heart.

'We ended up stopping about fifty different men. We'd tell them that we'd received reports of men engaging in acts of gross indecency, and took their details. Some of them would tell us, yes, they come here looking for sex. We would ask why they didn't go to gay clubs or pubs, and they'd say those places weren't their scene. It was a full range of ages. Men who'd driven there from up to about twenty miles around. The vast majority of the men we stopped were married or had girlfriends. There was one incident when we saw cruising going on in the park near the toilets. An older man and a much younger man, sizing each other up. They went into the rhododendron bushes...'

Araminta doesn't want to hear any more, but doesn't know what to say; how to stop him talking.

'The squad waited about thirty seconds, then went to see what they were doing, and they were tossing each other off. We arrested them both for gross indecency in a public place. The old guy was a grandfather. He said, "But I bring my granddaughter down here at the weekend", as if that was some sort of defence. The other was a young guy in his twenties, who said, "You're not gonna tell my girlfriend, are you?" They were both cautioned. We didn't press charges; we were there as a deterrent. It was the peak of the eighties, at the height of the AIDS epidemic and there were decades of repressed homosexuality. Homosexuality became legal in 1968, but it still wasn't tolerated for a very long time. Having sex in public was still gross indecency whether it was heterosexual or not, but the charge was almost always used against men. There was definitely a certain homophobic tinge to the police. I hated it. I pretended, like the others, that I was doing it with glee, but it made me feel ashamed inside. I had friends who were gay. I'd gone to drama school, for God's sake!'

Toby waits for Araminta to smile, but she doesn't.

He assumes she's gripped by his story. 'What did we achieve? It was legally correct, but it was petty. Sometimes, we used to take them home in the police car and drop them off outside their front door, just to wind them up. The men said they did it for the thrill; because of the possibility of being found out. Some *did* want to be found out. Once, we drove one back to Secret Street, although luckily that was before I lived here.'

'It wasn't before I lived here, though', says Araminta. The words have slipped out before she could stop them.

'What d'you mean?'

'I'm sorry, I just need to pop to the loo.'

Araminta hurries to the Ladies. She stands at the basins and stares at herself in the mirror. Her face is swamped with anger. She has never hated anyone more than she hates Toby right now. She washes her hands in cold water, just to be doing something, anything, to try and distract herself. There are signs advertising quiz night and darts night. Ordinary things that ordinary friends do together; not a cuckolded wife having to listen to a policeman merrily recount the day he brought her husband home in a police car and ruined the rest of her life. She'd been right all along: friends are too much trouble; it's better to keep oneself to oneself. She'll make an excuse and leave.

***

35 years ago

'Mum!' Becky was yelling from her bedroom down to her mother in the kitchen.

Araminta left the pan of Bolognese sauce where she was stirring it on the stove, and walked to the foot of the stairs to call back up to her daughter, 'I've told you about shouting. Please come down and speak to me; don't yell like a fishwife'.

'But Mum, Dad's come home in a police car!'

Jenny was in the kitchen, doing her maths homework, and jumped up and ran to the front door. Araminta opened the door, just as Becky had run downstairs, to find Fred standing on the doormat, but making no attempt to come in. The policeman in the car, who'd just dropped Fred off, waved and drove away.

'He waved', said Becky, as if that was somehow important.

'Come *in*, Fred', Araminta said. 'What on earth is going on?'

Fred walked into the hallway and stood, looking down at the hall rug.

'What's happened?' asked Becky.

As Fred lifted his face, he didn't quite make eye contact with any of them.

'Just leave us a minute, girls, will you?' said Araminta.

'But we want to know', whined Jenny.

Araminta looked at Fred's expression. It frightened her; reminded her of the time he'd had to tell her her father had died suddenly of pancreatic cancer. As she looked at him, she incongruously felt a wave of passion. He was so handsome. The kids at school called him 'Jesus' because he had long brown hair, which he wore in a pony tail, somehow managing not to look daft, and a neat beard, which framed his beautiful, gentle face, and set off his deep green eyes. He was slim-hipped, muscular, quite tall at six foot, and always dressed well. Right now he was in a white cotton fitted shirt and Levi's.

'Come into the living room, Fred.'

He followed her dutifully into the living room of the Secret Street house they'd saved up together to buy, ready to have a family.

'Look at me, Fred; what's happened?' Araminta sat down on the green velour sofa, but Fred remained standing the other side of the glass coffee table. He took a deep breath in, then out, then looked towards the door. The girls were both still standing there.

'Go to your room, Becky', said Araminta. 'Go back to the kitchen, and finish your homework, Jenny.'

Both girls stomped off and slammed their respective doors behind them, one after the other. Araminta winced.

Fred remained silent.

Araminta firmly closed the living room door, shutting out the sound of the ticking clock in the hall. 'We can't just sit here – stand here – whatever, in silence all night. Talk to me, Fred.'

Fred appeared to be Velcroed to the carpet. 'I've been caught cottaging', he whispered.

'I don't understand', said Araminta.

'Cottaging is when men meet in public toilets and...'

'I KNOW WHAT COTTAGING IS, YOU FUCKING WANKING WAZZOCK! she thundered, lapsing into her West Country accent, frightening herself with her uncontrolled anger, which seemed to be shifting the ground beneath her.

'I...', he began, 'I...'

'So does this mean you're gay?'

'I think I might be.'

'You're goin' out cottagin', and you think you might be gay?'

Fred said nothing.

'Gettin' yourself arrested', Araminta continued. 'Why cottagin'? Couldn't you just go down the pub, or somethin'?'

'Well, I...'

'You done it before? How long has this been goin' on?'

'Well, about, maybe... a year... or two.'

'Oh, that don't matter. What matters is did you think you might be gay the last time we made love? Did you?' Fred remained silent.

'Did you think you might be gay when you impregnated me with our daughters?'

'Well, I have felt afraid to confront my feelings for...'

'*Your* feelings? What about *my* feelings? What am I? Your cover? What are the girls? An experiment?'

'I'm sorry.'

'Do you even love us?'

'Of course I do.'

'Do I need an AIDS test? Do the girls?'

Fred opened his mouth, but no words came out.

'My *God*, Fred!'

'Mum', Jenny shouted from the kitchen, 'the dinner's burning'.

Araminta burst into raging tears that seemed to burn her face as they flowed down her cheeks. 'This whole marriage is a joke; a fake', she sobbed.

'Mu-um', yelled Jenny, 'the dinner!'

As Araminta wiped her sleeve across her wet face and headed for the kitchen, in a low voice, Fred said,

'But you're a fake, too'.

Araminta pretended she hadn't heard him as she looked at her sauce; now a black, congealed, hissing mess. It was unsalvageable.

***

As Araminta comes out of the toilets, Toby is right in front of her. 'It was your house, wasn't it? I'm so sorry; so terribly sorry.'

Araminta crumples down onto the nearest seat and bursts into heavy, ugly tears. Toby reaches behind his back to take his rucksack off the handles of his wheelchair, fishes inside for a pack of tissues, and hands them to her. Araminta takes one and thanks him. The couple in the corner look over, then quickly away again. The man at the bar pretends to be engrossed in his newspaper.

'I didn't want you to leave without me saying sorry. I am so terribly, terribly sorry. I shouldn't have done it.'

Araminta looks at him. He's telling the truth; he *is* sorry. He looks as if he's in pain.

'You must hate me', he says.

'Well...' Araminta takes a deep breath, sighs, and collects herself. 'You *have* already said you didn't want to do it; that you felt bad about it at the time.'

'I did; I truly did, but I still could have resigned.'

'You could, but you were young, and doing what you were told.'

'Well, I was, but that wasn't why I joined the police; to torture people. I wanted to make their lives better, not worse.'

'You were right, though. Ultimately he *did* want to be found out. It gave him that opportunity he'd been waiting for to tell me he was gay.'

'So he left you?' says Toby, immediately wishing he hadn't; it was too harsh. He isn't interrogating a witness now.

'Yes, in the end, he left me for a man. I was such a fool; how could I have not known that my husband was gay? He performed adequately in bed, I suppose. But how could I have not seen it? All those years. I was never enough for him. If he'd trusted me – had any real respect or regard for me – he would have told me. And respect has to be earned, doesn't it? I just wasn't a good enough wife.' She looks directly at Toby. 'And I don't think it's your fault. He wanted to be caught. He'd been trying to tell me that he wanted to leave me for over a year; waiting for the right moment, and you provided that moment.'

'I know you're saying that to be kind, and I appreciate it. But I want you to know I wasn't that happy about it at the time, and right now I really am truly sorry.'

'You were just doing your job.' He looks so crestfallen, Araminta's initial anger has almost disappeared and she feels sorry for him. 'It's just occurred to me', she says, 'that it must be difficult to make friends if you live in the community you police'.

'Well, you get one hundred per cent for empathy, Araminta, because, yes, it's a nightmare. That's why a lot of police officers try to live as far away from their patch as possible. And we used to have police bars – social clubs – of course, because we couldn't relax in pubs. If you have a couple too many, people will gossip, "I saw this policeman, and he was pissed." If you're nice to your wife, they'll say, "Policemen are all henpecked."'

'Well, I'll admit to you now, Toby, that I have been making a special effort to make friends.'

'It can be tricky, can't it?' says Toby.

Araminta nods. 'Yes, I suppose it can.'

'Especially when you think you're making a friend and the person turns out to be your nemesis.'

'You're not my nemesis.'

'I still feel terrible', Toby says, shaking his head.

'Look; tell me something you *are* proud of, from when you were a policeman.' The chef must have arrived and turned the fat fryer on in the kitchen, because the smell of chip fat was starting to waft invitingly around the pub.

'You sure?'

'Yes, let's cheer ourselves up a bit.'

'OK, well, something I *am* proud of is when I was called to Ashford International; you know it? It's a multi-track station, where some trains pull into the platforms, and others whizz straight past.'

Araminta nods. She definitely feels better, and smiles to Toby, fishes out another tissue from the little pack he'd given her, and blows her nose.

Two teenagers had run away from a children's home, and a report came through that they had been seen on Platform 6, via CCTV. A station guard was keeping an eye on them as they walked down to the end of the platform. One was dressed like Madonna in *Desperately Seeking Susan*, with baseball boots, baggy black jeans and a black bomber jacket. She had a defiant mouth painted with red lipstick, and long blonde hair in a black velvet hairband'.

'You have such a good memory!'

'Police training. The other had short, gelled-up brown hair and wore blue jeans and a denim jacket. They both had enormous earrings. When they saw me – I was in uniform then – they ran across each set of tracks into the centre. Trains were coming and going at speed. Each track, of course, had a live rail. The station guard was yelling, "Come back! Come back now!", but the runaways were just standing there. The short-haired one was visibly shaking with fear, but the Madonna one was gripping the other's arm, not in fear, but to stop her running back to the platform. I got halfway over to them so they could hear me, and called out, "Come back, you can see it's not safe. Please come back." To my immense relief, the short-haired girl snatched her arm from the other's hand, and daintily picked her way across the tracks back to the station guard, who helped her up onto the platform. But the Madonna girl was yelling, "Fuck Off! I don't care; I wanna die anyway." The guard shouted, "There's a fast train coming in sixty seconds!" I had to step over the next two sets of train tracks. When I reached the girl, she said, "I'm too scared, I can't do it." She was crying now. I think it had dawned on her that the wonderful adventure had ended and officialdom had caught up with her yet again. I said, "Come

on, I'll help you", and held out my hand, but she wouldn't
take it. The guard on the platform shouted, "You have no
more time; you must come back now!" So I said, "I'm going
to have to carry you, and you're going to have to cooperate.
If you muck about when I'm carrying you, you'll kill both
of us." She let me pick her up in my arms. She smelled of
cheap perfume; a scent like a cross between pink roses and
strawberry jelly. She wasn't heavy, but as I stepped over a
live rail, she leant down to try and touch it. Her hair blew
into my eyes and mouth, and I had no free hands to pull
it out. I jerked backwards so her outstretched arm couldn't
reach the rail, and one of her hooped earrings caught on a
button on my uniform. I had to keep going; trying not to
drop her...'

'Oh, but you didn't, though; drop her?'

'I really thought I was going to, but, no. It was a huge
relief when we made it back and up onto the
platform. She was taken back to the police station.
Sometimes I wonder where she is now. We were often
taking kids back to children's homes. The homes were
always chaos. There'd be the supervisor – usually
somebody fairly young – and kids would walk past and give
them abuse. There was no discipline; it must have been
horrible for staff and residents alike. The kids were always
running off and being brought back.'

'How heroic you were, though! Like Clark Gable carrying
Vivien Leigh!'

Toby laughs. 'It was hardly *Gone With the Wind*, although
there was quite a backdraft from that through train.'

'Did you get a – what's it called – a commendation?'

'I had various commendations. Not for that. I got one
for chasing a burglar up a drainpipe onto a roof; a few

that involved running. There might have been a fight outside a nightclub when one of the offenders runs off on seeing the police. I would run after them and topple them in the street. Shoplifters in shopping centres; I'd run after them. I always caught them. Apart from being handy for chasing after suspects, my running was a great release. I'd reached a point that I found it relaxing. I had what they call a "runner's high". It was no effort at all; I used to feel as if I was gliding on air. Especially when I was out in the countryside; I almost felt as if I was on a cloud, my head felt so light.'

As she listens, Araminta thinks of the painful irony of being told this by a man in a wheelchair.

'I know what you're thinking', says Toby. 'The good thing about it, though, was I was becoming disillusioned, and it turned out I didn't have to make a decision to leave the police force; it was made for me.'

'The accident, you mean?'

'Yes.'

'D'you want to tell me what happened? Was it dreadfully heroic?'

'Erm, no, in a word', Toby laughs. 'I was at home, outside my house, up on a ladder three storeys high, painting the carved fascias and the... what do you call it? The sticky-up pole bit on the gable?'

'The finial?'

'Yes, the finial. I'm not really one for DIY, but I wanted to get this done because Hils is quite house-proud. She's good at DIY, but scared of heights. She'd mentioned the finial was looking shabby. It was a fiddly job, and took much longer than I had anticipated. When I finished, I was up at the top of that forty-foot ladder, so thrilled with myself for doing it, and thinking Hils would be pleased with me. Then I stepped back to admire my work.'

Araminta gasps. Then she looks at Toby. He's starting to laugh; belly laughing. His chair is shaking almost as if it's giggling, too.

Araminta smiles, then throws her head back and guffaws. 'Oh, lawks, sorry, are you sure it's OK to laugh?'

'Laughter is the best medicine. And it *is* funny.'

'The enormity of it, though.'

'Falling from a height like that was a very odd experience. It can't have taken more than a second or two to land on the stone slabs of our garden path, but it felt as if I was falling for ages. There was a strange, dull thud which I realised must have been me, and a sort of melodic clang from the paint pot. I landed in a kind of V-shape, buckled at the middle like a rag doll. I anticipated pain, but there was none. From my waist down, I couldn't feel anything at all.'

Araminta takes a deep breath, and blows the air out, loudly. 'What happened next?'

'Hils found me, poor woman. I've done so much to stress her out.' He sighs. 'I was in Pembury Hospital for a while, then after the scans, they knew my back was broken and I was transferred on to the spinal unit: Stoke Mandeville in Buckinghamshire. I expected it to be full of old people, but the other patients were mainly younger people who'd broken their backs doing things like horse riding, scuba diving, or coming off their motorbikes. My mum came to visit expecting me to be a mess of cuts and bruises, but there was barely a scratch on me.'

'Hang on', says Araminta, 'my round, yes?'

'If you like. Hils is working, of course, so I'm just kicking my heels, so to speak. Only a half this time, though.'

Araminta returns from the bar with Toby's half and a ginger beer for herself. She doesn't want to risk drinking much more alcohol at her age.

'Thanks', says Toby, taking a slurp of beer. 'I was in the spinal unit for about six months. They taught me how to move myself about, and how to get in and out of a wheelchair. I wanted one of those chairs a bit like disabled sports players use; fast and lightweight. People think I got it on the NHS, but I had to buy it myself. My mum did a sponsored run to help raise the money. I can take it apart and put it back together myself.'

'Yes, I've seen you do that.'

'It was a great excuse to have a sports car, not only because they look good and drive well, but because they have a very long front door, so I can wheel myself right up to the opening, lift myself into the driver's seat, take the wheels, then the seat off the chair (the back folds down), then reach behind me to store it on the back seat while I drive. I have to have an automatic, of course, and I have hand controls attached to the foot brake, and a knob on the steering wheel so I can turn it with one hand. It's difficult when some selfish able-bodied driver decides to park in a disabled space; it often means I can't park at all. I don't need the space to be near the shop, or wherever I'm going; I need it to be able to put the wheelchair next to me, so I can get myself in and out of it. Many times I've wanted to go somewhere, but I've had to turn around and go straight back home again because there's nowhere suitable to park.'

'That must be all kinds of infuriating.'

'Just a bit. There was one occasion when I was going to Sainsbury's, and there was only one disabled space left. As

I pulled slightly past and stopped, ready to reverse in, a man, who looked about sixty, promptly drove forwards into it behind me. I just looked at him, puzzled. The man got out, all beige anorak and righteousness, and announced, "I did that because you're not disabled!" My hair had grown quite long while I'd been in the spinal unit, and I suppose in Anorak Man's opinion someone in their thirties with long hair driving a three-litre Toyota Supra doesn't look as if they could be disabled. As it happened, someone drove out of the space next to me, so I stopped, wound down the car window and asked Anorak Man to wait; said I wanted to show him something. He looked confused, but stood there politely as I reverse parked, opened my door, and started to get my wheelchair out. Anorak Man didn't say a word, didn't apologise, just walked on into the shop. But when I came around the end of the cereal aisle and saw him again, he dropped his basket and fled.'

'Wow! People can be so ignorant!'

'Actually, another incidence was last weekend, when I went to the tip to get rid of a broken ironing board and microwave. Hils doesn't like driving, so we left the wheelchair in the house and put the junk in the back seat. Then at the tip, I was still in the driver's seat, of course, and Hils was getting the microwave out when some clever spark said, "Typical of a bloke to get the woman to do all the work!" That stung a little. Then there's that indignity when we're out together as a couple, and someone will say to Hils, "Does he want a drink, too?" and she'll say, "Why don't you ask him?"'

'Uggh!'

'Yes.'

'Ignorance again. So many people need to be educated about so many issues.'

'Some people *do* try. One of the physiotherapists proudly told me how, as part of their training, they have to spend a full day in a wheelchair, and go out shopping. That upset me. I know they're doing their best to empathise, and I appreciate that, but the point is that at the end of that training day they can stand up and get out of that wheelchair. I will never be able to do that – never.'

Araminta desperately wants to say something helpful; nourishing. But all she can think of is, 'I'm so sorry, Toby'.

'We're getting a bit maudlin now', says Toby. He thinks of other things that aren't very nice to talk about. He won't be telling Araminta those. One of them is having to sit on the toilet for half an hour each morning with disposable blue latex gloves on, waiting for bits of poo to come down so he can fish them out of his backside with his finger. And talking of excrement, it's really unpleasant when he's out, and gets dog shit on his wheels, then it gets all over his hands. He has to wear gloves, and carry disinfectant wipes with him. For weeing, he wears a sort of condom, open at the lower end and attached to a tube, which attaches to a leg bag with a sort of plastic tap at the bottom that he can open to empty it. Quite handy, though, when he's on a long car journey, or when out and about, because he can empty it down a drain and no one knows what he's doing.

Even more private, is sex. Thank goodness there are more ways than one to satisfy a woman. Hils has been brilliant, in fact, almost smug when explaining this sort of thing to her closest girlfriends. But she was upset when one of them said that they couldn't live with a disabled man. She was more upset about it than Toby was. Especially with Hils being a nurse, Toby's determined to be her husband, her lover; not another patient.

Araminta's finishing her drink.

To break the silence, Toby says, 'In the spinal unit, one of the nurses said she couldn't believe how stoic I was being; that it was alright to cry. But what's the point in that? I just have to get on with it. Maybe I use that emotional numbness I learnt in the police, I'm not sure. I *have* noticed that the people who take longest to get over becoming disabled are the ones whose accident was caused by some kind of negligence, or when it wasn't their fault. They're angry, and the anger makes it harder for them to accept the situation and get on with their lives. With me, it was no one else's fault; just typical stupid human behaviour – forgetting for a moment that I was up a ladder.'

'That's interesting; the anger thing.'

'My disabled life's really not so bad. I've just had to adapt. Our house had three storeys and a basement, which was now no use to us, so we sold up and left No. 19 at the top and moved to our maisonette at No. 98 at the bottom. I have a wet room I can use for showers, and we had some of the kitchen worktops lowered so I can chop vegetables and make coffees and do bits and bobs in the kitchen. Luckily the houses in Secret Street already have lovely wide doorways and corridors, and I get from the ground to the first floor on a stairlift, with an indoor wheelchair waiting for me at the top. It works.'

'So that's when you gave up policing?'

'The police were very good. They gave me a job in the control room. So, dealing with a lot of the same things, but at a distance, I suppose. I didn't miss opening the morgue, or being bait for cottaging, or moving on homeless people, but the control room was still infusing me with that jaded view of the world. I took early retirement as soon as we could afford it. Hils loves being a nurse, so she's still working.'

'Is it OK to ask what you miss most?'

'About being a policeman?'

'No, about being able-bodied.'

'Oh, right, well, I miss running; getting out and about on my own, feeling the blood pumping – that runner's high. And I suppose it *would* be good to walk barefoot and feel the grass beneath my feet.'

A tear appears in Araminta's eye. She looks down at Toby's feet. His brown suede monkey boots look as if they've just come out of the box.

Toby sees her looking. 'Yeah', he says, 'they don't get much wear'. He chuckles.

'I'm so sorry, I shouldn't have asked.'

'It's fine. People think being paralysed, being in a wheelchair, is just about not being able to walk, but it's all the other things, too; things you can't do any more that people don't think about. I could have had it worse. I could have died when I fell off the ladder.'

'One can always find someone worse off than oneself', says Araminta. 'Princess Diana was driven far too fast, by a driver way over the limit, into that tunnel in France, and came out in an ambulance.'

'Hils says it's tragic that Diana finally found love, and then died.'

'Beyond tragic.'

'It's interesting, though; in one of the leaflets they gave me in the spinal unit – the one about sex and relationships – it says if you didn't have trouble attracting partners before you were paralysed, the chances are you won't have trouble now. I'm the same person; it's just that I'm on wheels. With my useless lower body, it's as if I've become a merman having to drag his tail about on land. Once I painted my face brown, pulled myself into a brown sleeping bag, hoiked myself into my wheelchair, put deely boppers on my head, and went to a fancy dress party as a slug.'

They laugh.

'Becoming paraplegic changed me physically; made me disabled. Being a policeman changed me mentally. You could say it made me emotionally disabled.'

'Oh, I wouldn't go that far.'

'Since I left – and other ex-police officers I've talked to about this say the same – there's been a softening of my emotions. That can only be a good thing.'

Araminta exhales, loudly. 'Wow! Well, I have learned so much talking to you!'

'Learned who arrested your ex-husband, you mean?'

'No, silly. You've taught me about anger. I should stop being angry with myself about my ex. And never mind my childhood, but I need to stop being angry about that, too. But we'll leave that subject for another day. Another year, maybe.'

'I can't take any more booze, not if I'm going to be awake when Hils gets back.'

'Yes, we'll go. Thank you so much; I've enjoyed your company.'

'I'm grateful you let me apologise', says Toby, undoing his brakes.

They call out, 'Thank you', to Stephen.

Toby wheels out through the back door, crosses the car park to the pavement, and as he wheels back home, Araminta walks beside him.

The Bicycle

75 years ago

On a grey Christmas Day morning in 1947, six-year-old Ivy
Brown picked up the hem of her nightie, jumped down the
stairs as fast as she could, and ran into the dingy parlour,
where she'd hung her stocking – an old flesh-coloured
Lisle one of her mother's – from the mantelpiece the night
before. The stocking had three exciting bulges. Beneath it
stood a small, red bicycle, with matching red stabilisers
bolted on. Attached to the handlebars with string was
a label made from an old brown envelope that her mother
had cut into the shape of a holly leaf. Ivy eagerly read the
label. *Michael*, it said. She felt a flicker of disappointment,
but the little red bike was too babyish for her, anyway;
Michael was only three. Ivy grabbed her stocking and
savoured every second of feeling it, trying to guess what
was inside. Apart from boiled sweets now and then, the
only treats they had throughout the year were presents
at Christmas and birthdays. The lump at the top was soft
and spherical. Ivy pulled it out to find a lovely, juicy
orange. It smelled tangy and wonderful. Beneath it were
two dense, slightly jagged lumps. Whatever sort of toys
could feel like that? She fished one out. It was a cold, hard...

...stone. She tipped the other lump out on the floor. Another stone. She stared at the stones, sitting there on the rug. They scowled back at her. Then a loud wail of a cry burst from her quivering mouth. Ivy left the orange there with the stones, and ran upstairs towards her bedroom, which she shared with Michael, sobbing loudly all the way. Reaching the landing, she could hear her mother's voice through her parents' closed bedroom door.

'You didn't ought to 'ave done that.' Not shouting, exactly, but raised. Ivy stifled her sobs and pressed her ear to their door.

She heard her father reply, 'She needs to learn not to expect nothin''.

'You only done it 'cause we ain't got no money.'

'It was either that, or we 'ave no turkey. We 'ave to 'ave a turkey. We can't 'ave tripe an' onions like usual, not on Christmas.'

'But Christmas is about the children; not your stomach!' exclaimed her mother. 'What'll she be thinking?'

'That she's been bad, an' 'as to do better.'

Ivy thought she heard one of them walk towards the door, so she darted into her bedroom, sat on her bed, and wondered what she could have done wrong. She forgot to tidy the bedroom last week, so that might have been it. No, it must have been something much worse. Then she thought of her dolly. Ivy had two dolls; one plaster, the other wax. The plaster one had a pale blue dress her mother had made for it, and embroidered the name Ivy had chosen – Becky – on its white pinny. Becky's eyes were closed when she lay down, and opened when Ivy stood her up, except one of them stuck a little, which gave the impression she was winking. She had called the wax doll Jenny. Jenny was smaller than Becky, and her face, to be honest, was a little odd, with the eyes a bit too close together, but Ivy loved her all the same. One night Ivy had sat playing schools with Becky, Jenny and Michael's teddy, and had left them all by the fire when she went to bed. The following morning, Ivy had found Jenny with a little lake of melted wax attached to her face where her nose should be, and her hands and toes were melted, too. Ivy had cried then, even more than she'd cried this morning.

Michael was stirring. She didn't want to infect him with her misery, so she wiped her face on her nightie, and gave his opening eyes the biggest smile she could muster. 'It's Christmas, Michael! Come on; come downstairs!' Michael's smile was as bright as the Star of Bethlehem as he realised what day it was, and Ivy held his hand as he awkwardly clumped down the stairs to the parlour. It helped cheer Ivy up. No one could look at Michael and feel miserable. Young children are supposed to be jealous of their new siblings, but Ivy had loved Michael from the moment he'd been born in the middle of the night on his parents' bed. Her dad had come back from the war "peculiar", people said, as if all the light had gone from his eyes. But when Michael was born, Dad was happy, and that meant everyone was happy. It didn't even matter so much when Dad hadn't been paid again for one of his plumbing jobs, and it didn't matter when the house was grubby because their mother was too tired to clean their own home after spending all day cleaning other people's.

When Michael saw his bicycle, he did a little dance on the spot. He tore off the label, commanding, 'Read, Ivy, read!'

'You know this, look, it's M – I – C ...'

'Michael!'

'Yes! Want to ride it?' Michael jumped up and down.

'We have to get dressed, though, to go outside. Come on; upstairs, quick!'

In their bedroom, Ivy helped Michael into his little flannel shorts and fair isle pullover. She wished she had a nice dress, but her school blouse and pinafore would have to do. It was all the family could afford, and her mother washed it when it was dirty, and hung it in front of the fire on the airer to dry overnight. Ivy put on her shoes, and helped Michael into his, tying his laces for him. Back downstairs, they put on their grey duffle coats, and Ivy wheeled Michael's bicycle down the hallway's brown lino and out into the cul de sac. Michael climbed into the seat and looked up expectantly at Ivy.

'You do it like this. Put your foot on 'ere, and push.'

Michael pushed the pedals the wrong way so they span backwards.

'Forward, like this...' Ivy pressed his foot in the right direction on the pedal, 'It goes round and round, see?' The bike jolted forward and Michael squeaked with delight.

'Look, there's a bell, but don't ring it now; it's a bit early; you don't wanna be wakin' folk.'

Michael rang it anyway, as his parents emerged into the front garden and onto the pavement to watch him. As Ivy's dad proudly gazed at Michael, Ivy thought about how he'd not thought twice about announcing to Ivy that he always wished she was a boy.

Ivy's mum came and gave her a hug. 'You ain't been bad, love. It's just 'is way. I wanted to get you another dolly, but we only 'ad enough for the bike and the turkey. It was 'is way of... It's 'is pride, you know? 'E wa'nt always like this, 'e come back from the war different, you know; not 'imself.'

Her mother gave Ivy a final squeeze, and went back inside to start cooking the Christmas dinner.

At lunch time, when Ivy had finally talked Michael into leaving his bicycle outside and coming in to eat, he was still the happiest she'd ever seen him; his cheeks rosier than ever. After lunch, he was allowed to go back outside, while Ivy was expected to sit and listen to the wireless when King George gave his Christmas speech. The King sounded so lovely, Ivy thought, and she imagined what it must be like to be royal; to be a princess and have all the dresses you wanted, and presents for Christmas as well as a turkey, and brandy for the plum pudding, which they always ate, not after their main course, but after the speech, to eke out the enjoyment of the special food. By the time Michael had found his thruppenny bit, his face was redder than the holly berries on the mantelpiece.

'Come 'ere, Michael', said Ivy's mum, 'let's 'ave a look at you...' She felt his forehead, 'Oh dear Lord...' then pulled up his pullover to reveal his chest stippled with red spots.

Scarlet fever. There was no money for a doctor. Dad must have brought it from the Shepherd's house where he'd been fitting a new bathroom, because one of their younger children had it, but they'd called the doctor, and the child had pulled through. Before they heard Big Ben chime midnight on New Year's Eve on their wireless, Michael was dead. They didn't even have money for a proper funeral, and Michael was buried in a cheap pine box in a pauper's grave, above two other impoverished dead people. The following summer, Nye Bevan created the NHS.

Michael had left his bicycle outside the house, next to the front door. Nobody dared touch it, as if moving it would somehow erase their memory of him. So that's where it stayed; the red paint gradually fading to a dusty pink, the little silver bell, first peppered with, then devoured by rust.

After that, Ivy's mother became a kind of robot. She still went about her cleaning jobs, and chatted – apparently cheerfully – to the wealthy ladies she cleaned for. News had spread of Michael's death, and people felt sorry for her. Some avoided her and crossed the street to the other side because they didn't know what to say. Others came over to say things like, 'He's in Heaven now, dear little cherub', or 'Remember the good times', none of which helped.

As well as hiring Ivy's dad for plumbing jobs, the Shepherds also employed Ivy's mum as a cleaner. They lived in a big, detached house on the edge of town, and Ivy used to go and play in the fields behind it. The Shepherds had four children, the oldest a daughter, two years above Ivy at school, called Jean. Everyone knew Jean; infamous for being short-tempered and thoughtless. Behind her back, they called her 'Mean Jean'. Jean's best friend and next-door neighbour, Araminta Cavendish, couldn't have been more different, and people wondered why kind Araminta hung around with Mean Jean. Mrs Shepherd gave Ivy's mum Jean's old blazer for Ivy, ready for senior school. It was a bit too big for Ivy, and had a small ink stain on one of the pockets, but it was much better than having no blazer at all.

On the first day at her new school, Jean and Araminta saw Ivy in her oversized blazer in the school dining hall at lunch time.

'Oh look, everyone', announced Jean, 'look at the new girl in her enormous jacket! Isn't it sweet?' and grabbed the edge of the blazer, waving it around, as if to show everyone. Then Jean spotted the stain. 'Oh my goodness, look at this; Ivy Brown has *my* old blazer! You'd think her mother would have scrubbed the stain out, what with her being a charwoman.' Jean laughed like a cracked bell.

Ivy ran out of the dining room.

Araminta followed her out. 'Don't mind Jean', she said, 'she doesn't mean it. It's just her sense of humour. Come back in and have your lunch'.

Ivy meekly followed Araminta back into the dining room, and sat down to have her school dinner: a sausage in a bread roll, and an apple.

After lunch, Ivy went with the other new girls to her lessons. Still smarting from Jean's outburst, she thought, 'I'll show her! I'll show that Jean Shepherd I can be just as posh as she is'.

The teacher asked what county they were in.

Ivy put up her hand to answer, and when she was chosen, instead of saying, 'In Zomerzet, Miss', in her guttural West Country accent, she tried to sound like Princess Elizabeth. 'Taunton is in the county of Somerset, Miss', she shrilled.

The other children laughed.

'Really, Ivy!' exclaimed the teacher. 'Don't be silly; you're only a plumber's daughter.'

Some people might have given in, but Ivy Brown was determined to better herself. She worked hard at school, and managed to get a place at a small teacher training college near Tooting. In the evening, she took elocution lessons; practised changing the shape of her mouth to create the correct vowel sounds, repeated sentences like, 'The lady gave me the plate on Thursday', and softened her Somerset "S"s to remove the "Z" sound. Maybe, because the change was gradual, her fellow students didn't notice her new way of speaking. Maybe they were too polite, or too embarrassed to mention it, and giggled about it behind her back. Either way, Ivy didn't care, she was becoming the young woman she wanted to be. When she qualified, she took herself to the crown court for deed poll forms. Two days later she returned, and five minutes' Bible-holding and affidavit-swearing later, she left Ivy Brown inside, and emerged from the court as Araminta Cavendish.

She couldn't be Araminta in Taunton, and had no desire to return there, anyway. She thought about where Araminta Cavendish would live. An advertisement for a newly qualified teacher in a small spa town, about fifty miles south-east of London, caught her eye. Where better than Royal Tunbridge Wells?

Lavender

The Otter Inn –
Stephen's Story

1971

In a grey corrugated iron chapel in a small outback town in New South Wales, little Stephen climbed up to the pulpit to read from the big black Bible. It was thirty degrees outside, and thirty-nine inside the metal church; the doors closed to keep out the flies. As he bent down to push the wooden box from the back to the front of the pulpit, sweat glued his white shirt to his back beneath his blue linen jacket. He stepped up onto the box so he could reach the lectern, and stretched his neck up to try and make space behind his starched white shirt collar, which was buttoned up beneath his blue Sunday tie. He didn't understand why it was called 'the lesson'. Surely lessons were for school. Maybe God wanted to teach the congregation a lesson. He opened the Bible at the page his father had marked, and – knowing he had to sound grown-up and sombre – began to read.

'Luke, Chapter three....' Sweat trickled down his forehead and onto the page, where it dripped onto the *6* of *verse 16*. 'John answered them all, saying, "I baptize you with water, but he who is mightier than I is coming, the strap of whose sandals I am not worthy to untie."' Stephen wished he'd been allowed to wear sandals, instead of his Sunday best brogues. He continued, 'He will baptize you with the Holy Spirit and with fire'. Stephen closed the Bible, and said, 'This is the word of the Lord'. As the congregation chorused, 'Amen', he looked over at his mother, sitting in the front pew with his father, who was wearing his white vicar's cassock. She didn't smile, but nodded her approval. He clambered back down from the pulpit and went to sit next to his parents.

After church, he sat politely with his sister, Deborah, in the parlour, waiting for Sunday lunch, which was eaten after saying grace, and in silence. It was as if someone had embroidered one of those samplers that was supposed to say *Home Sweet Home,* but somehow got it wrong, and sewn *Emotions Forbidden* instead. Crying, specifically, was not allowed, nor were feelings to be discussed. What was important was decorum; to be a model family.

Little Stephen (never Steve) and Deborah (never Debbie) had been told they were adopted before they set off on their first day at school. Not that the word "adopted" was used: they were "chosen" and should be grateful. Chosen children had a duty to live a sober and Christian life.

Once, Stephen and Deborah were sent to stay with Uncle Bob and Aunt Tilly for a few days. Their aunt and uncle loved children; they loved fun; they loved life. Reverend Williams only allowed Stephen and Deborah to read classic novels, but here they were allowed comics, to chat noisily while they ate their tea, and to grub around at the back of the yard looking for treasure with no worries about getting their clothes dirty. They found tiny pieces of opal, glinting like miniature, toy universes, and back in the house, they were allowed to try a cup of tea for the first time. When Reverend and Mrs Williams came to pick them up, they didn't want to leave.

The little town where they lived was on the edge of the Blue Mountains. Whenever he could, Stephen would run down the myriad walkways worn into the warm sandstone cliffs, deep into valleys feathered with giant green ferns, through the blue haze from the eucalyptus trees, through the echoes of cicadas, cackles of kookaburras and the shrieking of the lyre birds. Here, he was Steve. His best friend was Noel, a cool kid with an American dad and a buzz cut. At school they were baseball stars; Steve the pitcher, Noel the catcher. Here in the bush, they'd tunnel through the ferns, making dens. Often, they'd fling off their plimsolls and paddle in the cool, clear water pools that collected at the foot of the waterfalls thundering down the valley sides. The boys knew to keep their heads bowed to look for leeches that would slime up their shorts, and yabbies – pesky freshwater crayfish that might pinch their toes. On land, the threat was snakes: red-bellied, copperhead and tiger. Some of them could easily paralyse a child with one bite. Funnel web spiders lived in the crevices of rocks, and if one of them got you, it was curtains. But Steve and Noel were skilled at seeking out the snakes and spiders, and would play safely all day long, until Noel's mum rang a bell that echoed across the valley. Then they instinctively knew their way back, always circling round and up to the left until they were back at the top of the cliffs, and home.

Reverend Williams was Australian. He'd met his English wife while stationed in England in the army, married her, and brought her back to New South Wales. When Stephen was thirteen, Reverend Williams and family emerged from the little local cinema, blinking into the sunlight after watching *The Railway Children*. The English countryside, its lush green hills and sweeping rains had locked themselves into Mrs Williams' mind, and she was homesick. A few days later, Stephen and Deborah were told they were moving to England.

Stephen reacted by setting fire to a bush outside the house. Luckily Mrs Williams came out to hang out washing at just the right moment, or the fire could have been catastrophic. But moving to England *was* catastrophic for a thirteen-year-old boy whose character when away from the house, and free, *was* the Blue Mountains; laughing with the kookaburras, scurrying into fern dens with blinking-eyed, dinosaur-shaped lizards, breathing the blue haze of eucalyptus while the lyre birds made whatever sound they damned well pleased.

The Williams family sailed on a passenger ship from Sydney to Southampton. In the hold beneath them were their grand piano, harpsichord, twenty tea chests and a washing machine. They weren't coming back.

Reverend Williams' new church was an unremarkable building opposite the gasworks on one of the hills above Bath. In the seventies, Bath wasn't considered the elegant city it is today. Its buildings, all built in honey-coloured Bath stone, were black with diesel fumes and glowered, rather than glowed. To Stephen, the pavements, shops, and squares seemed to be packed with far too many people; about eighty thousand of them jostling for space in an area similar to the little town the Williams' had just left with a population a tenth of the size.

Stephen's new school was a gothic monster. Spherical topiary puffed with pride as he approached the huge, iron-nailed front door, and inside, the dark oak panelling of the grand halls glared at him. It felt as if the pupils were there for the building, not the other way around, and that building seemed to swallow Stephen up. Most of the pupils were boarders, and the timetable reflected that, with the school day lasting twelve hours Monday to Friday. Saturday morning was lessons again, and sports in the afternoon. Sunday, of course, was taken up with church.

The boys laughed at Stephen's drawling Australian accent, and he started to learn to sound more English – posher – to avoid the ridicule. Back in his little outback town, he'd often been top of the class at school, his bedroom mantlepiece aglow with certificates, medals, and books he'd been awarded at school prize-givings. But it seemed his schooling back in Australia had been two years behind his English public school. Instead of coming top of the class, he began to fail. Every day, he would trudge to school and back past the gasworks, then cut down away from the clatter of the busy, industrial road to walk alongside the muddy green river, which bore no comparison to the waterfalls and pools back home. Instead of the cliff edge paths up the Blue Mountains' valleys, diesel-blacked terraces peered blankly down at him. One evening, just past a bridge, and by a green gate belonging to the end house of a terrace that butted the riverside, he saw an otter on the path. For a while, it considered him as if somehow they had an understanding. Then, with a gentle splash, dived into the river and disappeared, leaving rippling circles behind it that gently widened and flattened until you'd never know it had been there.

Stephen met his mother's family. Aunt Sarah, Uncle Bill and the cousins were all lanky, with a distinct head shape and long, thin noses. Stephen's face, his build, felt more wrong than ever. He was stocky, with a rugby player's neck and dark curly hair. He didn't belong. To make matters worse, outside their front door were giant planters of blossoming lavender, filling the air with a heady scent that – although it's meant to be calming – somehow always stuck in Stephen's throat and made him feel claustrophobic and anxious. He inhaled noisily before walking past them, then tried not to exhale until he was inside with the front door safely shut behind him, running to the back of the house where it was safe to breathe in again, followed by stares from thin-nosed relatives, and embarrassed throat-clearing from his mother.

For a treat, Uncle Bill took Stephen and Deborah to the seaside. They were used to day trips to Bondi Beach, Manly, and Surfers' Paradise, with miles of platinum-coloured sand, and warm, turquoise seas. Blasted by chilly sea breezes, Bognor's sea was slate grey and icy, its beaches made of pebbles that hurt the soles of Stephen and Deborah's feet. Dubiously, they waded out. Stephen trod on some sort of blubbery lump of meat; a butchered fish that a fisherman must have chucked overboard.

Stephen watched *Cleopatra* at the cinema. Elizabeth Taylor had dark curly hair, and dark eyes, like him. The paparazzi had been having a field day over the stormy relationship between Elizabeth Taylor and Richard Burton, with headlines like, *Love... Lust... and Liz,* Stephen fantasized that maybe he could be the secret love child of one of Liz's affairs.

The Williams family went on holiday, travelling around Europe in an uncomfortable Lada hatchback. When they stopped in Italy, Stephen felt at home among the friendly locals, who rewarded him with smiles and encouragement when he tried out a few Italian words. Warm, relaxed people, with dark, curly hair like his. Surely his mother must be Italian – a lively, affectionate, dark-haired beauty?

Stephen never caught up at school. He ended up with just one O Level. His parents made no attempt to hide their disappointment. He had failed to fulfil his role of perfect, redeemed son. Maybe just to spite them, Stephen decided to try and be an artist, and managed to get a place at an art school in London, emerging with a certificate in art into Thatcher's Britain with four million unemployed. He drifted from one job to another, eventually becoming a barman in the Jolly Porter in Stall Street. It was good, honest, mind-game-free work, and supplied a steady stream of amiable locals to chat to. He enjoyed playing host, and it gave him some idea of what role he was supposed to be playing. He and his girlfriend, Sally, were both as lost as each other, but they could at least be lost together. They decided to marry, as that meant they could take up a tenancy and manage their own pub. It made sense at the time. They took on a country pub, the Royal Oak, in a small town in Somerset, not far from his parents' house. Their son, Mark, was born two years later.

Having a child gives rise to doctors' questions about genetic legacy: was there any family history of heart defects? Kidney problems? Mental illness? Sally was keen for Stephen to trace his biological parents. They ordered the necessary papers, but with the forms in front of him in black and white, Stephen concluded that whatever his idle curiosity, he couldn't imagine what it might be like for a woman to have to give up her child. It must be a desperate situation, perhaps involving violence, or rape, poverty, or mental illness, and surely his poor biological mother wouldn't want all that dredged up. Crucially, he didn't read all the way down to the small print that said he could register that he didn't want to be contacted. Looking back on it now, he wonders how his life might be different if he had.

1961, Australia

The evening sun fell awkwardly on the Clareville Home for Unmarried Mothers, creating shadows behind the veranda. A gecko scuttled away from the doorway in search of warmth. This maternity hospital, in a suburb of Sydney, New South Wales, was run by the Salvation Army, and powered by righteousness. All the staff knew what was best for the mothers and their unsuspecting babies. Nadine, seventeen, with a dying mother and three younger siblings, had never had the talk about the birds and the bees, and didn't realise that a moment of passion with her boyfriend, Tom, would result in her being here, nine months later, sent away from home to have a baby. Keeping her baby was never an option, in fact, unmarried mothers were told that it was best for the child to be given away to a married couple – a deserving couple – and that keeping it would mean they didn't love it. It was never acknowledged that giving up a baby might have emotional consequences for both mother and child. What was important was to avoid the shame – the stigma – which infused the sinful unmarried mother, and infected her whole family; the whole community. Nadine's sisters and brother had no idea what was happening to their big sister; they were told she had gone away to work.

At the formal adoption interview with the home's Salvationist authorities, Nadine and Tom fidgeted awkwardly in their chairs. The adoption officer deliberately omitted to tell them financial support was available should they wish to keep their baby. And crucially, neither were they told that there would be an option to revoke the adoption should they change their minds. The emphasis was on what they believed was best for the child, which meant acting according to the Salvation Army's ideals. With some kind of strange attempt to appear to respect them, Nadine and Tom were allowed to say what kind of parents they wanted to adopt their baby.

'People who are kind', said Tom.

'Loving', said Nadine, 'and not religious'.

'No', agreed Tom, 'not religious'.

'And we want to call him Tom', Nadine added.

When Tom was born, Nadine was allowed to keep him with her in the unmarried mothers' home for a fortnight. She would gaze into his dark brown eyes, feeling her milk spilling through the bandages the nurses had bound tightly around her breasts, feeding him with formula milk from a hard, glass bottle. She told herself what the Salvation Army had told her to believe; that she was giving him away because she loved him. She picked some lavender from the garden and smuggled it into his cot. Maybe so he would always remember her when he smelled it, perhaps being pushed in his pram somewhere in Sydney. Maybe so she would always remember him when she smelled lavender – his dark, curly hair, his tiny fingers that gripped hers.

The Australian Reverend Williams and his English wife were friends with Clareville Home for Unmarried Mothers' presiding doctor. In fact, the doctor had trained with Reverend Williams' GP father. After three miscarriages, The Williamses had decided that God had chosen them to redeem two bastard children by adopting them. Reverend Williams told the home's doctor that they would like the next healthy boy that was born. Tom and Nadine's request for a secular upbringing for their child was ignored, for why would anyone listen to the opinions of sinners? Reverend and Mrs Williams were considered perfect, and baby Tom was handed over, renamed Stephen, and Nadine sent home in a haze of shock.

In her follow-up appointments with the Clareville Home doctor, Nadine would ask about her baby. 'Is he well?' 'Is he happy?' 'Are his adoptive parents kind?' As time went on, Nadine manufactured reasons to see the doctor, just so she could sneak in questions about her baby son, so the doctor telephoned Reverend and Mrs Williams. 'The mother's becoming increasingly desperate for news. I thought I should warn you. Obviously we must do what's right for the child...'

Six weeks later, Reverend and Mrs Williams had found a parish in Surrey that needed an Anglican minister, and they were on a ship to England with baby Stephen. A year later seemed the perfect time to finish creating their model family, and blonde-haired, blue-eyed baby Deborah was adopted. Three months after that, they returned on the ship to Australia.

1995

Stephen was pouring a pint when the phone rang. He grabbed the receiver with his spare hand. He was supposed to have gone to his parents' anniversary lunch three days previously, but hadn't bothered, so was immediately on the defensive when he answered to find it was his mother. 'Never mind that', she said, 'we've just received a letter; a letter for you from your natural mother in Australia'.

Stephen's knees buckled. He slid to the floor, where he sat staring at a bucket of empty bottles, while beer spilled out and over the pint glass above him.

The phone call had changed everything; whipped his existence from beneath his feet; left him reeling. Stephen had to get to his mother's to read his letter from his mother. There were no appropriate words available for him to either speak or think. From this moment in his life, the word "mother" became loaded with both love and anxiety. Now he had two mothers that required differentiation: the mother who adopted him, and the mother who gave birth to him; his "natural" mother or his "adoptive" mother. And none of the words were right. "Birth mother" can be offensive to a mother whose child was ripped away from her, and who is, especially at that moment, so completely a mother. Yet the mother who changes nappies and cooks meals and nags about homework is also wholly a mother. Soon Stephen had said the word "mother" to himself so many times that it came to mean nothing at all.

Sally was delighted, and insisted he should go and read the letter immediately. A few hours later and he was perched on the uncomfortable sofa in his parents' front room, speaking the usual bland formalities of, 'Hello, how are you?', then waiting silently with his father while his mother went to make tea. He could see an envelope on the table with a row of tell-tale red koala-themed Australian stamps across it. A letter stuck out with photograph edges visible. Stephen tried to break the silence,

'Well, this is a turn-up for the books, then!'

'What's that?' his father replied.

'The news from Australia.'

'Ah, yes, that.'

To his father, it was as if Stephen was talking about something as inconsequential as the weather, or bin day. Stephen's mother allowed herself to show more excitement than her husband as she brought in the tea. There were two letters, she explained; one to Stephen and one to them. Theirs was short, with a brief explanation from a woman called Nadine Jackson that she had obtained their address from the Church of England, and that she was Stephen's natural mother, and hoped, if it were possible, they could forward on a letter to him. There was a brief description of her life of marriage to an American man, two further children, and success running restaurants in Sydney.

There was a photo. The woman smiling out from it looked like Stephen.

Stephen took his letter in his hand. He was helpless. There was no way of knowing what it was going to say; no way of preparing himself. Whatever his mother had written, he knew it would change his life forever.

The handwriting was a little like his. He steeled himself and began to read.

Dear Stephen,

It feels strange to write to you as Stephen because I named you Tom. The thing I must say first is that I have always loved you, and thought of you every day of my life, and hoped that you are happy...

Stephen was unable to stop himself – he sobbed. Through his tears, Stephen read, while Reverend and Mrs Williams sat stiffly in their high-backed chairs.

...When you were born, I was only seventeen, and your father, Tom, was nineteen. My mother was very ill and died soon after. My father was left with five children to raise, of which I was the eldest. I wanted to keep you, but my father wouldn't allow it, and there was no way I could have looked after you on my own. When you were adopted I was told you were going to a good and loving home. I have lived each day with the hope that this is true, and that you have always been showered with the love I was unable to give you...

Nadine's letter went on to explain that she and Tom broke up a year after Stephen's birth, and that in due course she met a lovely man, Duncan, and got married. They had a daughter, Annie, and a son, Andy. When Annie was eighteen she went to art school. When Stephen realised that he had two half-siblings, they looked a bit like him, and one of them had gone off to art school at eighteen, just like him, it was too much. He thought he would never stop crying.

...There are so many questions I want to ask you. Are you married? Do you have any children? What career did you follow? Do you live in Somerset, also? It is such a beautiful part of England...

...Stephen, I will say goodbye for now, but I would love it so much if you would like to write to me or telephone. I would be so happy to hear from you.

With all my love,

Nadine Jackson

Stephen's mother seemed happy, read his letter, then exclaimed, 'This completes the circle!' His father muttered discontent about the Church of England giving out their address without any proper checks.

Back at home, Sally and Mark were fascinated. They spent hours looking at photographs of the Jackson family, pointing out, 'Look, she stands like you', and 'Now we know where you get your hair from', and, 'You have her brown eyes'.

Stephen had to somehow find the concentration to work that evening, knowing that because of the time difference, he couldn't phone Australia until the early hours. He realised he cared deeply for his natural mother. He wondered if he always had. He was conscious that letters took five days to arrive from Australia, so Nadine's hopes and fears would be playing havoc by now. He had to contact her quickly. She lived in Manly, a suburb of Sydney where he and Deborah often used to have days out at the beach. He phoned the number at eleven o'clock at night, to coincide with breakfast time over there. He knew from the letter that Nadine was going to be on her own, which was helpful, as he had also read in Nadine's letter that none of her family knew about him, including her husband, Duncan.

When the phone was answered and Stephen said, 'Hello, is that Nadine?', he pronounced her name in the English way, with a short first syllable.

'Yes, it's Nadine', replied the Australian voice, pronouncing it 'Nay-deen'.

'I had a letter from you today, and I wanted to say thank you, the letter made me very happy, and that I am Stephen Williams, your son.'

There was a slight pause, a sharp intake of breath and a shriek, and then they introduced themselves over a conversation that went on for three and a half hours, trying to cover thirty-eight missing years – school, college, work, marriage, children...

Stephen learned that Tom had also married in Sydney, and had a son, but that was all Nadine knew. Annie, Stephen's new half-sister, lived in New York. Andy, his new half-brother, his aunts, uncles, and their families, all lived in the Sydney area.

'I've been looking for you for at least eight years', said Nadine. 'It involved going through state records individually, so I hadn't realised that you'd left for another country. I hadn't wanted to tell anyone – not my brothers and sisters, nor Andy and Annie, nor my husband, Duncan, nor my friends – about your existence unless I actually found you. There was no point in risking upsetting them for nothing.'

Stephen wasn't sure how he felt about his existence upsetting people.

'My father told me it was my sin that had finally killed my mother. In the early sixties, children of unmarried mothers were kept secret. I refuse to use the word "shame"; the shame was never mine, but imposed on me by others – the Salvation Army, the doctor, my father. Even though my experience of being your mother was supposed to be shameful, to me, it felt like love; excruciatingly painful love, but love, all the same.'

At the end of the call Stephen knew he wouldn't sleep that night. He went out to walk through the little country town at four o'clock in the morning. Stephen had been found. He'd been so very, very lost, and he was found. It was hard to let the milkman puttle by on his milk float without stopping him and showing him the photos he was still gripping, saying, 'Look! Look, it's my mother! My real mother!' How could the hedgehogs just toddle past without stopping to marvel at what had just happened? Everything about the world was changed; new. As he turned the corner back to his pub, above the rooftops of the little parade of shops in the high street, he saw the morning sun's first rays of light.

Over the following weeks there were more letters and phone calls. Nadine said she would visit in October that year to coincide with her birthday. It arrived quickly. What was the protocol for meeting a long-lost mother? Sally and Stephen decided it was best if Nadine had her own space, so they booked her into the *Holiday Inn* in Bath for two days, then, once she'd had a little time to get over her jet lag, in a nice holiday rental in the town. When the day came, Stephen's stomach flipped somersaults as he drove to the hotel.

He opened the hotel room door to a big hug from a short woman whose eyes and face looked almost the same as his. As they sat on the hotel bed and talked, looking at photographs of family – *his* family – he marvelled at the total love and affection coming his way. He didn't have to do anything for this love – read in church, pass exams, be quiet and godly – it was his, unreservedly. His ambivalence about being adopted was swept away in the face of the thirty-eight years this woman had spent grieving, wondering, questioning; not knowing what had happened to him. He held a birthday party for her in the pub, and some of the regulars joined in, congratulating them on their discovery. It was a lovely event, full of laughter and excitement.

There was afternoon tea with Stephen's parents, which both sides had requested, but conversation was hard work and interrupted by several loud silences. His mother's initial pleasure seemed to have fizzled out, and his parents seemed to be regretting the legal turn of events that had caused this reconciliation. They were of the generation that had signed a document declaring a finality they never imagined would be reversed. As they left, Reverend Williams said quietly in Nadine's ear, 'I'm a Clareville boy'. Safely away from them and in the car, Stephen asked her what he meant. 'Never mind', she said, her eyes full of anger, or sadness, it was impossible to tell. It was only months later, when she was back at home, that Nadine plucked up the courage to explain. Reverend Williams was part of the suburban elite; a vicar, the son of a doctor who had trained with the Clareville doctor who had chosen Stephen as "the next healthy boy", almost as if he'd been out shopping. It was that Clareville connection that had stopped Nadine having any chance of having her boy back. What Reverend Williams meant was, Nadine couldn't have her baby back then, and she couldn't have him back now.

Nadine stayed at Stephen and Sally's for three weeks. When Stephen was working, she came along and sat in the pub until closing time, accompanied Stephen to collect Mark from school, then installed herself in the pub again for the evening shift. Stephen had begun to be overwhelmed by her, and started cutting himself off from his family and responsibilities. He missed the annual village party, which upset several locals. He never had a spare moment alone with Sally and Mark, and Sally began to be wary of a woman who seemed to want Stephen all to herself; who introduced herself to their perplexed eight-year-old as his new grandmother – a grandchild role that he couldn't play as it made no sense to him. To make matters worse, Stephen and Sally were short of money, and Stephen's insistence that he must save the fare so he could go – alone – to Australia to meet his new family made it clear to Sally just how unimportant they really were to each other.

Then the time came for Nadine to leave, and Stephen felt the thud of anticlimax. All that fantasizing about Elizabeth Taylor or a warm-lapped Italian mother was gone. He'd experienced the true unconditional love of a mother, but as he waved her off at Gatwick Airport, and saw the last corner of her yellow wheelie suitcase disappear through the barrier behind her, he was left with his loveless existence, his broken marriage, and nothing in his life seemed to have really changed.

As the time went by after Nadine's departure, Stephen received emails and phone calls from the extended family. The news of his existence had caused seismic shocks throughout the family in Australia and America. There was a general disbelief from her siblings, from her children, from all those around Nadine, at how she had kept all this secret; why she had not confided in those close to her. Andy and Annie were furious with their mother, both for keeping such a thing from them, and for depriving them of a relationship with their half-brother. Stephen resolved to go to Australia to meet them all the following year. It would take a good few months to save up. This would be the first time he'd gone back since he left as a boy.

The twenty-four-hour flight from Heathrow to Sydney is usually gruelling, but Stephen was so excited to meet his mother – his family – in Australia, that somehow the hands of his watch twirled clockwise with a magical speed. At the airport arrivals lounge, Nadine and Duncan were waiting for him. Duncan was charming. Stephen wondered how he'd coped with finding out about this son that had existed before his own children. Duncan seemed more baffled than angry.

For twenty-five years, Stephen had pined for Australia, bitter as a teenager about being dragged away from his home, fantasising about a place he didn't know as an adult. Basking in the heat, hearing the kookaburras again, smelling the eucalyptus in the air, he was home.

Then began introductions to a *lot* of people. Stephen was introduced to his half-brother, who was also overwhelmed to meet the face behind the voice. He was taller than Stephen, and more like his father. They instantly hit it off. Stephen met cousins and uncles and aunts and friends of Nadine's. The timetable was relentless. Day after day, Stephen was being paraded. He was the lost son; the miraculously found son; the dinner party story.

Stephen managed to negotiate with Nadine to see his adoptive family's relatives – his cousin Tricia and her husband – who lived in a fabulous house where she'd brought together all the family on Stephen's father's side for the occasion. Tricia wanted to show Nadine that Stephen already had family before Nadine appeared. Nadine was uncomfortable; Tricia triumphant.

Then came November, and a trip to New York for a weekend to finally meet his half-sister, Annie; a sort of blonde version of him. They bonded right away. It was a new kind of love for a woman that he'd never encountered before: that of a man for his sister. One of Annie's gripes to her mother about keeping Stephen secret was that it was possible, if they had met – not knowing they were half-siblings – they could so easily have fallen in love and married. Feeling the easy, refreshing love Stephen felt for her, it was a scenario that wasn't as ridiculous as it might at first have sounded; something that's actually happened to a few poor, unsuspecting lovers.

Two years passed. Stephen's marriage of convenience to Sally had fizzled out. He'd left the pub and got a job working for the council in London, where he lived in a bedsit in Herne Hill. He took a month's unpaid leave, and flew to Sydney for a Jackson family Christmas in Manly in forty-degree heat. When Nadine, Duncan, Andy, and Annie arrived at the airport to meet him, the atmosphere made Stephen wince. They'd chosen that journey – the first time they'd all been together since Stephen had appeared in their lives – to tell their mother all her shortcomings. They couldn't forgive her for hiding such an important secret. They understood now why they'd been pressured to be perfect, with the perfect schools, perfect dance lessons, perfect clothes, but nothing they had ever done had been good enough because they could never even begin to match up to the longed-for golden child. Andy had been told how disappointed they were in him for being gay and ruining their chances of having a grandchild. Annie, still single, had been chided for messing around with art school, not becoming a successful artist, not settling down into marriage, nor having a successful career, after all that expensive schooling. The traditional Christmas beach picnic deteriorated into Nadine praising Stephen and dismissing Andy and Annie's demands for an apology, for understanding; some resolution to their anger and frustration. Nadine tried to justify her behaviour; reminded them how she'd been stitched up by the Clareville Boy and his wife.

'They're scum!' she bellowed.

Stephen couldn't bear it. With all their faults, his parents were the people who'd done their best to bring him up as best they could. Rightly or wrongly, they were suffering from the same ridiculous notions of righteousness that the Salvation Army and much of Australian society in general held at the time.

'They're not scum, you can't say that!' he shouted back.

Nadine screamed, 'Fuck Christmas!' and stormed off.

Duncan burst into tears.

Stephen was supposed to be staying for a month, but he booked the next flight back home. At Heathrow Airport, he bought a bottle of Johnnie Walker on a maxed-out credit card. The bus fare home from Heathrow was seventy pence and he only had fifty, so he walked the twelve miles back to his dingy bedsit. He spent that New Year's Eve alone.

Stephen had two mothers. One who brought him up, whose coldness was the best love she could muster, whose expectations he could never live up to. Her love was about making him the person she felt he should be. On balance, though, it still felt as if maybe she was his "real" mother. His natural mother – his birth mother – loved him unconditionally, but hers was a dreamlike love in which he was the golden child in a relationship tinged with so much emotional pain and resentment, so much brokenness, that when he was with her she constantly changed the subject of every conversation to herself and her own suffering. She *had* suffered terribly, God knows she had, but it felt to Stephen as if *he* was the parent in the relationship with the responsibility to look after her, not the other way around. Thinking of it this way, he wasn't sure what he'd gained from meeting Nadine.

Waking up from the dream of a perfect mother was painful. Stephen had always carried his adoption with him on his shoulders like a hod loaded with rejection. He tried to lighten the load by coming up with sentences that began with 'At least': At least he hadn't ended up in care, like those Barnardo's boys shipped over to Australia and – some of them – brutally abused. At least his biological mother had tried to find him, and loved him in her own way. At least the mother who brought him up had done the best she could. But the load never lightened, and he often found himself walking with his head bowed down, as if in shame. When people commented on it, he told them he walked like that from being a child in the bush, and having to keep an eye on the ground for snakes and spiders. That was at least partly true.

The summer after that disastrous new year, Nadine phoned. She spoke so fast; it took a few seconds for Stephen to work out what she was telling him.

'I've found Tom; I've found your father!' she exclaimed.

Stephen didn't share her excitement. Tom may not want to be found. Fathers play a small role in creating a child compared to mothers. He tried to slow her down a little by explaining that he simply couldn't afford another trip to Australia to meet Tom; it would take a long time to save up again.

'But he's not here', she said, 'he's in England!'

'No! Where?' Stephen asked. Nothing could have prepared him for her answer:

'Bath!'

The hairs stood up on the back of Stephen's neck. He was excited, but confused. This was too much of a coincidence.

'He's lived there since the seventies. Gloucester Terrace; the house on the end, by the river.'

It was the house Stephen had passed every morning and evening on the way to school; the house with the green garden gate. The house where he'd met that solitary otter. He'd spent his life believing his real father was nine thousand miles away in Australia. Each time Stephen had walked to and from school, they were no more than nine metres apart.

Tom and Stephen met in Browns, the same restaurant in Bath where Nadine and Stephen had their first meal together, and sat at the same table – the window seat at the front. Tom had Stephen's mannerisms, or maybe that should be, Stephen had Tom's mannerisms. Tom was reserved, like Stephen. The conversation was polite, cautious. At one point a tear escaped from the corner of Tom's eye, but as he fumbled in his jacket for a tissue, he excused himself, 'Sorry, I have this eye condition...'

They both chose the same Rioja to accompany their meal, and they both drank a little too much, a little too fast. Stephen nipped to the toilets, only to be confronted with lavender-scented hand soap. Too late, he took a breath in, then laughed aloud at himself.

With identical, deep, gentle voices, two strangers – father and son – talked of their lives, each taking care not to upset the other.

After the meal, they stopped talking altogether, and sipped their Irish coffees in silence.

Then Tom put his glass down.

'The Bath thing, though; you growing up here, not in Oz; both of us being in the same country – the same town all along – no one would believe it.' He shook his head and chuckled.

'No', said Stephen, putting his glass down, 'no one would believe it'. He shook his head and chuckled, too.

Silently, side by side, they gazed through the restaurant window. Outside in the city streets, cars, buses, and people went who-knows-where, who-knows-why.

65B Secret Street – Ian, the Old Barnardo's Boy

Eleven weeks before the party

'Oh my goodness, a castle!' exclaims Araminta.

The black and white photograph depicts a dour-looking castellated monstrosity of a building, complete with turret, battlements, and tower.

'Yes', says Ian.

Later, Araminta will Google *Comlongon Castle* to find it was built in the 14th Century, had a prison, guard room, and dungeon, and came complete with a ghost: the "Green Lady", who had thrown herself from the tower after being forced into an unhappy marriage. It seems a forbidding place to bring up young children.

Ian's brought his photograph album, as promised at their last conversation when he'd come to do his regular weekly gardening, pruning Araminta's hedges, and weeding her borders. He always stopped in for a cup of tea and a shortbread afterwards, and Araminta had asked him if what she'd heard was true; if he was a Barnardo's Boy.

'That is not correct', he had replied, 'I am an *Old* Barnardo's Boy.'

Now here he is in her front room, his tweed flat cap and gardening coat hanging on the hooks in her hallway. He's showing her an old, red photograph album. It has black cartridge paper pages and photographs carefully attached with little stick-on mounting corners, descriptions written in white beneath each one in old-fashioned handwriting. He's also brought a book called *Childhood Memories: A Photographic History of Dr Barnardo's homes.*

'So this was your first home?'

'Yes.' Ian shows Araminta a second photograph with children arranged in a long row, seated on a low wall in front of the castle. Boys with short back and sides haircuts, all in dark-coloured short dungarees, and girls all wearing light-coloured short dresses, with hair in identical ear-length bobs. Behind them are three women in nurses' uniforms, complete with white caps.

'Is it alright to ask how you came to be in a Barnardo's home?'

'Yes. Our mother was not – married.' Ian has a way of speaking with little pauses between his words – not a stutter, exactly, but perhaps a struggle to get the words out – which makes Araminta feel grateful for the effort he's making, just to speak to her.

'Father was – unknown. Miss White was a JP.'

'Justice of the Peace?'

'Yes, and she put us in the home; my brother and me.'

'I suppose there was no way your mother would have been allowed to keep you?'

'Can you see why this photograph was taken?' Ian's too excited about the next photograph to answer. His eyes twinkle and his grin spreads from his mouth to his ears as he turns the page to show two identical boys, about three years old, sitting beside each other. They're both looking desperately sad, bare-legged, their mouths slightly open, and wearing long-sleeved hand-knit pullovers. Behind them is a nurse in a white apron, holding up one of the boy's hands for the camera. The caption states *DAVID* beneath the baby on the left, and *IAN* beneath the one on the right, then below that, *AT WOODFORD 1945.*

'Do you know why this – was taken?' Ian asks.

Araminta carefully inspects the photo.

'Look at the hands and foot', Ian says, helpfully.

Then she gets it. 'Oh lawks, they each 'ave six fingers and toes!' forgetting herself and speaking in her West Country accent. She momentarily panics, then realises it doesn't matter. Ian's such a relaxing person to be with; he doesn't care what anyone sounds like, as long as they're kind.

'...was taken by the Barnardo's photographer.'

Araminta involuntarily looks at Ian's fingers.

He understands, and shows her the scar running from his smallest finger on the edge of his hand.

'They cut them off. In Wood Green and Southgate – Hospital.'

Araminta doesn't know what she thinks about that, so she changes the subject.

'So you're identical twins?'

'Yes.'

'What about temperament? Are you alike?'

'Oo, no, very different, very different. You wouldn't want to meet David; he's grumpy', Ian says, laughing.

'Oh, would he mind you saying that about him?'

'No, he would laugh, too.'

Araminta smiles.

The next photo is of the twins, aged about six, in shorts and short-sleeved shirts, holding hands; one smiling, the other frowning.

'Is the frowning one David?'

'Yes.'

Then a photograph captioned *MATRON*. She's a slim woman, in a dark uniform with a nurse's fob watch pinned to it with a sturdy safety pin. She wears a high lace collar gripping her thin neck, beneath a face with dark eyebrows, and hair pulled back into a nurse's white starched cap. Her lips are held tightly together as if she's trying to smile for the camera without looking happy, as if doing so would somehow betray her policy of strict discipline.

'Look at her prim little starched collar', says Araminta. 'She looks fierce.'

'Oo, very fierce!' Ian puts on his boy-afraid-of-Matron face.

'But the others look jolly.'

Ian turns to the next page. This photograph shows a dozen or so young children, all playing on identical small bicycles.

Araminta pushes away the memory of her brother, Michael, and wishes one of the boys in the photo didn't have the same name.

'Look, they've got little bicycles! They look so sweet! Oh; Peter, John, and Michael... they're all exactly the same bicycles. Well, they would be. Some of them look really happy; some of them look confused as if they're wondering what's going on.'

Ian doesn't comment, but turns the pages to a photograph showing four children aged about six or seven wearing long, stiff-looking greatcoats that reach down to the floor.

'Look at these coats, like army coats! Were they rough, those coats?' Araminta's becoming increasingly aware that she's speaking to this man tenderly, gently. It was something that seemed to just happen when speaking to Ian.

'Don't remember.'

Each child has their left hand in one of their coat's large, square pockets, and in the crook of each right arm is a soft toy: a teddy, a bunny, a puppy...

'Oh look, they each have a cuddly toy! Did you have one?'

'I don't remember.'

Araminta feels a little surge of sadness.

'Miss Bourne photographed them. This is the nurse that took us up and befriended us all the years until she died; Miss Bourne.'

'She was kind, and you remember her?'

'Yes.'

'Do you remember anything in particular she did?'

'She'd take us out to Southgate.'

'Oh. Was that a park?'

'Yes.'

'They all look happy when they're with Miss Bourne.'

'When Miss Bourne passed away, they gave me the photograph album.'

'Oh, I see; that makes sense. What a lovely thing to do.'

There's a page of three photographs of babies, captioned, *TREASURES ALL OF THEM*, as if the value of babies needed to be pointed out. One has five babies all in a row, with their names written beneath: *JANE. SANDRA. MICHAEL. SANDRA & CHRISTINE*. Araminta feels a lump in her throat. The next photograph is captioned PRAM *PARADE*; eleven nurses, each pushing a parentless baby in an enormous, black, Silver Cross pram.

Araminta wants to change the subject again. 'Do you remember anything about the homes – the physical building?'

'Oh yes! Oh very much! Outside was garden and fields. All built on now. There was a kitchen garden. And they always make us work; housework, cleaning, and gardening. You can't get out of it! Weeding, sweeping, clearing up.'

'Why only boys?'

'They do not mix. Don't know why. Only boys in mine; girls in the other.'

'Is it alright to ask, do you have any memory of ever meeting your mother?'

'Only once. I was about thirteen.'

'That must have been emotional.'

'Yes, very emotional. David and I don't really know her at all because we are backward.'

'Are you comfortable with that word, "backward"?'

'Yes, very much.' Ian nods enthusiastically.

'They did not call us Ian and David in those days.'

'What did they call you?'

'Cochrane!'

'But there are two of you, so how did they differentiate?'

'Cochrane One and Cochrane Two.'

'No!'

'I've got a double-barrelled name, Cochrane-Griffiths. Griffiths is Welsh and Cochrane is Scottish.'

'Where do the two names come from?'

'I know one is from my mother – Cochrane.'

'So where did Griffiths come from?'

'I do not know.'

Araminta can't imagine spending a whole lifetime not knowing where your surname came from.

'Anyway, so you were in the classroom. You were thirteen. Did you know your mother was coming?'

'No, she just turned up. The man from the house came up to the classroom; "Cochrane Twins, can you stand up, please. There's someone wants to see you down the house." We were both wondering who it was. So we went down there. There was our mother. But we didn't realise who it was. So we walked down to the fountain with her, then back up to the home. And that was the last time we saw her.'

'What did she look like? What did she say?'

'I can't remember.'

'Does that make you feel sad?'

'No, because we don't really know her; we don't know what she was like.'

'You were in a home in Southborough by then?'

'Yes. I'll show you; *Meadows Memorial*. Came there when eleven.'

Ian puts down the album and starts leafing through his book. With so much use, several of the pages have become detached from the spine. Ian carefully slides them back in. He lands at a page showing another large, austere-looking building. It has wisteria climbing around the stone porch, but in the black and white photo, the shrub looks black. The caption is, *Meadows Memorial Home/House/School, London Road, Southborough, Kent. Opened 1939 for boys over 11 years with learning difficulties.*

Araminta feels a penny dropping. Learning difficulties; of course.

'This is another scary-looking place.'

She immediately wishes she hadn't said that. It was up to Ian whether it was scary or not.

'Now, you'd remember this because you were old enough.'

'Not this one. Then we were in *Endurance* in Vicarage Road. That was another part of the brick building. Because we had three houses. There were three people looking after the boys. There were sixty boys. Twenty in each house. Mr and Mrs Evans used to look after us.'

'Were they nice?'

'Yes. Yes.'

'The Starling Farm was behind the house. They got chickens and pigs. We used to feed the chickens, and you know what we used to do? We had a big copper for the chicken food. And you put all the food in with a fire underneath it, for the meal. And you know what the boys used to do?' Ian beams at her, and uses his hands to mime taking handfuls of chicken feed from the copper and eating it.

'You used to scoop it out?'

'Yes, we used to scoop our hands in and scoff it. It was lovely!'

'Was that because you were hungry?'

'Not because we were hungry. It had everything in it. Meat.'

'So you ate it because it was nice?'

'Yes.'

'What was the food like – not the chicken food – the food in the home?'

'The food was very nice. But they gave me tapioca and I didn't want to eat it. So the next day the tapioca was back on the table. I got in trouble. The best thing was we took it in turns to wait on the headmaster. We had to wait on him and bring his food. His food was better than ours. But we'd get tips afterwards. You know how much money we earned? One and three. Spent it on our favourite sweets.'

'What was your favourite?'

Ian thinks for a bit, then replies,

'Mars Bar.'

'Did you have your own rooms?'

'*Broomhill*, about seven beds in a room. But the *Meadowhall* ones about fifteen or twenty. That building is not there now because they knocked it down and built a modern one.'

'You moved around quite a lot. Why was that?'

'Don't know.'

'That one looks quite beautiful, it's got a pretty veranda.'

'I didn't used to live there; I used to work there, because when I left school I used to work in the grounds. Gardening. Five years. And then *The Dell*. The head gardener passed away and they didn't want to have a new one, so the handyman became the head gardener. I didn't like him because he wasn't a proper gardener. So I'd be cleaning it up, and he'd come along and say, "Leave that alone!" And I said, "I'll pack up!" I went straight to the office, "I want my cards, please." And three days later, you know where I went to? Kent County Council. Groundsman.'

'And how long did you do that?'

'Forty-three years! In the parks. And then they put me to Sandown Park. The hedges wasn't going to be cut. They can't afford it. They asked a man to do all the hedges in

Tunbridge Wells by himself on the tractor and he said, "I can't do it." So he gave up. So that's why you don't see the hedges cut along Pembury Road and Dunorlan. There used to be five gardeners in Dunorlan Park. Only two now.'

'Did you have any particular friends at the homes?'

'Yes. Richard Andrews, one of the Barnardo boys. We used to go scrumping at Nightingale Farm.'

'For apples?'

'Yes. You come to *Hillyfields* on the right; it's just past that. I remember he had a little dog – a spaniel – that used to bark at us.'

'Do you think your life would have been better or worse had you been adopted. Do you ever think about that?'

'No. Can you find the one in Barkingside?'

Ian hands Araminta his book, and she looks in the index.

'Oh, *Australasian Medical Unit, Barkingside*. Would that be it? Why "Australasian"?'

'They send the children out. In those days, if they're clever, they send them out to Australia, and to Canada as well.'

Araminta feels a shiver down her spine. She doesn't want to tell Ian how lucky he is that he wasn't deemed clever, and sent to Australia or Canada where... she doesn't want to think about it.

'But you were happy? Being brought up in Barnardo's homes?'

'Yes.'

'What was the best thing about it?'

'Breakfast.'

Araminta smiles. 'I meant... I should have said, was it a good environment to grow up in? Was it nice there?'

'Yes, very very good.'

'I'm so glad.'

'I was there fifteen years, from when they took us.'

Araminta looks down at the book again and flicks back to the index. 'Ah, there it is; *Barkingside.*'

'That used to be the headquarters.'

'*Girls' Village Home.* Oh, it's beautiful! Why are you showing me this?'

'Because we used to go to the church there, and we used to have our annual meeting. And the pews are small.'

'Oh! Little ones for children; that's lovely!'

'Have you ever seen that?'

'I think I must have seen children's pews, but I can't remember where.'

'And there's the Stepney one; *Her Majesty's Hospital for Sick Children.* There was one little boy, in those days... Dr Barnardo was there and he refused to let him in because the place was full. And he passed away, And ever since, Dr Barnardo's say we will never refuse a child; *never.*'

'All these buildings! All these lives!' There's a picture of children lined up on a beach for the photo. 'Oh! Did you go to the seaside?'

'Oh yeah! Clacton.'

'Can you remember what you did in Clacton?'

'Yeah.'

'Did you swim?'

'Yeah. And when we lived in Southborough, we used to go down to Dymchurch; St Mary's Bay. There used to be a big army camp.'

'Oh, so you went and stayed there? Like a holiday camp?'

'Yes. All homes there. I remember one day we was in the dining room – big dining room – and we had our own tables. And there was a Roman Catholic table, and our table.'

'There was a ...?'

'Roman Catholic table. You can't mix. That was different homes. Catholic homes. And one day, they come with sausages on a Friday. They was brought to the Catholic table. "No, we don't eat those things!"'

'Oh! They could only have fish, couldn't they?'

'Yeah!' Ian chuckles.

'That's incredible, to think that the children were segregated – kept separate.'

'And I remember, once, they was having a dance, the Roman Catholics in the hall, and we were trying to get in. And they said, "Are you a Catholic?" "No, we're not." "Can't come in!" In those days, the Catholics separate.'

'So different now.'

'Yes, different. Once I *did* try and find my mother.'

It seems an abrupt change of subject. Araminta thinks maybe Ian's been thinking about his mother all the time he's been talking about miniature pews and sausages, or perhaps his mind simply flits about like that.

'When I was coming back from Scotland, I used to have a motorbike.'

'You came back from Scotland on a motorbike?' Araminta's used to seeing Ian cycling slowly but steadily up Bayhall Road towards the allotments. It's uplifting to imagine him young, leaning into a bend on a motorbike.

'Yes, I was passing through Kendal, and I saw *Dr Cochrane* and I thought, "I will go and find out." So I went to the surgery, and they said, "What do you want?" I said, "I'd like to see Dr Cochrane." She said, "Alright." She went in. She came back and said, "She doesn't want to see you."'

'Was that your mother? Or just somebody called Cochrane?'

'It was her sister. So I thought, "That was the last time. I'm not enquiring again."'

'Were you upset?'

'Yes. That she didn't come and show her face. Her father was a famous doctor in Kendal.'

'Ah, so that's how you knew it was the right Cochrane; because of the doctor connection?'

'Yes.'

'So how old were you then?'

'I was about seventeen.'

'What motorbike did you have?'

'A 125 Bantam.'

'Wow!'

'And you know why I gave up? I was beginning to wobble on the bike.'

'Why?'

'Eyes.'

'Oh!'

'And someone gave me a good idea of salt water.'

'Right.'

'I washed all the eyes out. And my balance went just perfect. So everything's alright now.'

'Good.'

'So, is that enough now?'

Araminta loves Ian's abruptness; his honesty. She'd asked him to tell her about his life as an Old Barnardo's boy, and he'd told her.

'It's really lovely of you, Ian, to bring your book and photographs and show me it all. Thank you.'

Ian nods.

'Will you come to the Platinum Jubilee street party?' Araminta asks.

'Yes. But first I will ring the bells at the church.'

'For the Jubilee? I didn't know you were a bell-ringer.'

'Yes.'

'I will think of you now, whenever I hear the bells.'

'I've been doing it for fifty years!'

'Wow! Oh, and what do you think of the Royal Family?'

'Very nice.'

'Do you remember Princess Diana or Margaret ever coming to visit Barnardo's while you were there? Because they were both patrons.'

'No, I was out in the wide world by then. Fifteen years ago we went to Buckingham Palace. Tea party, with Dr Barnardo's. It was very good.'

'What did you have to eat?'

'The best food we ever had! Sandwiches. All nice. Very excellent!' Ian beams.

'Little dainty sandwiches?'

'Yeah.'

'Do you remember what was in the sandwiches? Cucumber?'

'I don't remember.'

'And little cakes?'

'Yeah.'

'And proper tea in teapots?'

'Yes. But we noticed there were armed guards up on the building. We could see them. Watching, all the time. The

Queen wasn't there at that time. Princess Alexandra, she was the main guest.'

'What did you wear?'

'Everyone was dressed perfect. We wore our suits and the ladies are not allowed to wear trousers. They wouldn't let the women go in the palace gardens with trousers on.'

'Well, trousers will be allowed at the Secret Street party. And I don't think we'll need armed guards. Do you?'

'No.'

Ian stands up and Araminta walks him to the front door. As he's putting on his flat cap, and pulling on his old brown gardening coat, she can't help feeling she's been blessed by the presence of an angel.

Ian retrieves his bicycle from outside the front window, and fastens his bag with his precious book and photograph album in it onto the back.

Araminta wonders what it must be like to be so accepting of things; to experience the peace it must give to simply think, 'I don't know where my surname comes from, and that's OK.' To be comfortable with *not* knowing. To think, 'I am backward', and that's that; that's alright.

She calls out, 'Goodbye, Ian, thanks again', as he slowly cycles off, smiling.

A Bra Full of Fish Fingers

30B Secret Street – Nancy's Story

Her name is Nancy, and she has anorexia. Once it slithered round her, it would never let her go.

***

Nancy grew up in a home fogged with the unhappiness of poorly-suited parents. Her family was financially comfortable, but emotionally uncomfortable. Dad was a workaholic, and when he eventually arrived back in Tunbridge Wells from the City each evening, he didn't go home, but to the King's Arms. Mum was a housewife, and bored. She wanted to go out to work, but all Dad would say to her suggestions of jobs was, 'You should be at home with the children. I provide for everything; so what are you moaning about?'

Nancy was worried about them, and scared to grow up. She knew they only stayed together for the sake of her and her brother, Tim. She thought if she could stay a child forever, she could keep them together. Control issues already – anorexia liked that. Nancy was chubby. Short, with frizzy blonde curly hair. Maybe she was cute, but when she looked in the mirror and saw fat, or when the other kids at school called her "Fatty", or "Elephant Arse", anorexia readied itself.

She wasn't bothered that she didn't really have schoolmates; her best friend was her granny. Mum was great, and they got on together fine, but Granny was warmer, and cuddly. Granny and Grandad were no happier together than Nancy's parents, and spent their time arguing. So whenever they could, Granny and Nancy took comfort in each other. Evenings, weekends, holidays, were all spent having fun at the cinema, or shopping for colourful clothes, or trips to cafés for hot chocolate and Danish pastries.

One muggy July evening, Granny and Nancy were sitting on the sofa together, eating Strawberry Mivvis and watching TV. Coronation Street had just ended, and the credits were rolling up above grey tiled rooves and chimney pots. They'd been laughing at Jack Duckworth arguing with Vera, his spectacles held together with Elastoplast. Then, mid-sentence, Granny fell silent. Her mouth dropped open, and seemed to slide downwards at the side. Her head slumped onto her right shoulder. Then she was still.

Nancy's not someone who believes in ghosts, but she swears she saw something white – a bit like a twist of steam – leave Granny's body and float upwards, hover around the artexed ceiling, then disappear upwards. Just like that, her best friend was gone.

Nancy was in shock. She couldn't cry until the funeral. Then afterwards she couldn't stop thinking of Granny's coffin being lowered into the ground; the funeral directors in their long, black coats, braced against the weight. As they pulled the white lowering bands out from beneath the coffin, it had felt too final; too real. Scattering a handful of earth on the small, brass coffin plaque, Nancy felt she'd be alone now, for the rest of her empty, pointless life. That's when anorexia slithered around her.

As she worked through her shock, then anger, then misery, at Granny being taken from her, anorexia whispered in Nancy's ear that she'd feel better if she could lose a little bit of weight. Nothing drastic; maybe just cut out the cheese and onion crisps and Cadbury's Fruit 'n' Nut. She started to listen. It was just puppy fat, really, and she found it was easy to cut out the junk food. She began to have compliments at school: 'Oh, look how lovely and slim you're becoming!' 'What diet are you following?' She gradually felt better, as if she *could* keep going. Perhaps she *could* have a friend or two. Maybe she was beginning to be in control of her life.

Anorexia twisted its coils into a nest, and Nancy snuggled inside. She went to the library after school and looked at diet books. "Good foods" and "bad foods". 36 grams of fat in a pizza, 11 grams in a portion of ice cream... it was easy to identify what to avoid from now on. She learned calorie values off by heart. 55 in a portion of peas, but if she had lettuce, instead, it was only 8. No dressing, though; a dollop of salad cream is 42 calories, and has 3.45 grams of fat. At family meal times, she hid as much food as she could in her clothes: Chips – 424 calories, 16.6 grams of fat – down the back of her Levi's; fish fingers – three are 175 calories, 8.7 grams of fat – in her white Marks & Spencer bra. She collected it all into black bin bags, and stashed them in the back of her wardrobe, where they festered. She stopped getting the bus to school, and walked, to burn more calories. If she walked fast, she could burn about 200 each way. She lost more weight. Then more. At first, the shrinking was gradual, so her parents didn't seem to notice. Then it became obvious, and her mum started buying Complan supplement drinks to build her up. She'd wait till Mum wasn't looking, then pour them into a plant pot. Mum didn't understand why her spider plant seemed to be going mouldy. Mum and Dad started saying lame things, like, 'You were so pretty when you had a bit more weight on you', or 'The boys won't like you if you get too thin'. She didn't care, they could say what they liked. It was none of their business.

Nancy fell from fourteen to six stone that year. Her parents made an appointment for her to see the GP, Dr Pumphrey. He had an old-fashioned surgery, with brown leather chairs, and a big oak desk with a brown leather top, where he kept his stethoscope in a metal folding box, next to a pile of pamphlets full of prayers, entitled, *The Joyful Message*. While the big oak clock ticked loudly, and Mum explained her weight loss to Dr Pumphrey, Nancy sat glaring into her lap. His treatment? That they needed to pray. He sent them home with a pamphlet. Back home, Mum threw the pamphlet in the bin, and they sat on the sofa next to each other, in silence. Anorexia slithered tighter around Nancy, and grinned.

When Nancy brushed her hair in the mornings, her hairbrush grew fuller and fuller, her hair thinner and thinner, until her scalp showed through. She tried to encourage it to curl a bit more to cover the baldness, and took to wearing scarves and headbands. If her brother, Tim, wanted to wind her up, he'd say, 'Look at your hair; it's disgusting!' Her arms, back, and legs grew a fine furry down all over them. Her body was trying to keep her warm.

Nancy's mum kept trying. She offered her milky coffees, or hot chocolates, and sent her to the shop to buy cake. Nancy always chose Fondant Fancies because, even though they were sweet, they were small – 106 calories, 2 grams of fat. She'd take a pink one out of the box, and cut it into twenty pieces, then make it last hours. It drove her mum nuts. There were more trips to the GP, but nothing made any difference. When she looked in the mirror, Nancy still saw fat.

Then Dad found the bin bags. He grabbed one in one hand, Nancy in the other, pushed them into the back of his Jag and drove them to A&E. The car smelled like a refuse cart. At A&E, in the queue for Reception, Nancy began to panic. How was she going to get away with not eating now? Dad shouted at the poor receptionist, waving the black bin bag, which swung precariously from his hand, 'Look at this! Look at the state of my daughter! Do something!'

In a weird way, it was as if Nancy wanted to be caught. She knew anorexia doesn't mess around; it's the deadliest of all the mental illnesses. She didn't want to die. She didn't want all this attention, either; only to be able to get on with quietly controlling her life. But the hospital didn't admit her; just referred her back to Dr Pumphrey.

Then one day Nancy saw a photo: Nancy and her mum in the garden. Somehow, a photo carried more truth than a reflection in a mirror. It showed Mum in her multicoloured floral skirt, looking wide-hipped with rosy cheeks, and next to her an emaciated creature, its eyes somehow too big for its head, like something from those old black and white photos of prisoners in Belsen, or Auschwitz. But that creature wasn't a prisoner staring out from behind the bars of a concentration camp; it was Nancy, staring out from between anorexia's coils.

Nancy had no interest in anything. Nothing gave her pleasure; she was just existing. But seeing that photo was a tipping point, and she began to worry about what she was doing to her parents. She started to accept the milky drinks, and stopped hiding food in the wardrobe. Eventually, still nowhere near plump, but acceptably slim, she left school and went to catering college. There she could obsess about food as much as she liked. In fact, it was actively encouraged. She learned to fillet and dice, butterfly and bone, pare and purée. She learned to roast, baste, sauté, poach and coddle. She learned to create a tasting menu for twenty, or a banquet for three hundred people. She loved every minute of it, especially baking cakes for afternoon tea: walnut and coffee with rich buttercream icing, red velvet with cream cheese frosting, cupcakes decorated with sugar petals, leaves, and glacé cherries. She loved the measuring and mixing, flopping the soft mixture into big, shiny steel baking tins, the heavenly scent when she took the freshly-risen cakes out of the oven. But they weren't for her; they were only to feed other people. Nancy never ate a single mouthful.

In her early twenties, Nancy started work as a cook at *The Cavendish Hotel*. It was a wide building, three stories high, with pillars outside the front entrance. With its white rendering, she thought it looked a bit like a giant wedding cake. She loved walking past the front pillars each morning, hearing the swish of the polished glass revolving front door, and turning left at the back, by the car park, to go through the white gate marked *STAFF ENTRANCE*. She belonged there. She made friends among the kitchen and waiting staff. Sometimes on Saturday night, Rosie, Sally, Tina, and Nancy would go clubbing at Sticky's, or to see bands at The Forum. One night they went to see a local boy band called Shimma. The name was made up from the first letters of the band members' names: Shaun, Ian, Mikey, Matt, and Aaron. Five good-looking lads, each in a different pastel-coloured suit, singing catchy songs in pleasing harmony, while dancing impressively in formation. The one the girls all swooned over was the lead singer, Aaron. Nancy was a bit of a late developer as far as boys were concerned. She felt left out. She had no idea how to flirt, or to talk about boys, and, besides, she thought she still looked hideous, especially with all that hair all over her arms and legs. She didn't imagine she'd ever have a boyfriend, but she tried to fit in, and had to agree that Aaron, with his curly black hair and film star cheek bones, was dishy.

A month later, Nancy heard the waitresses chatting excitedly. They knew a new receptionist was due to start that day, but they hadn't expected it to turn out to be Aaron, from Shimma. 'He's so gorgeous!' they'd swoon, and try and find excuses to walk past Reception as often as possible. It was Nancy's job to take the day's "Specials" list for the menu to Aaron each morning, and he would chat to her, making jokes about the outrageously posh names for the dishes on the menu, or how he was convinced the head chef, Hugo, was on cocaine, or how the hotel manager thought no one knew his hair was really a toupée. Aaron made her giggle, but she rarely thought of anything clever to say; just found herself blushing and scuttling, tongue-tied, back to the kitchen.

A few weeks later, on her day off, Nancy was at home when the phone rang. It was Rosie.

'I've just had a very interesting conversation', she said.

'Oo! What? Who with?' Nancy asked. She picked the phone up from the side table in the hallway, and sat with it on her lap on the stairs.

'With Aaron!'

'About what?'

'About someone he's madly in love with!'

'Oh! I thought he was a Jack-the-lad. He can't actually be in love with anyone, not really...'

'He is, though...'

'Who's that, then?'

'YOU!' Rosie squealed.

This information didn't seem to fit in Nancy's head. There's no way Aaron could fancy her. He had a reputation for playing the field; he could have anyone he wanted. She didn't know what to say.

'Nancy?' Rosie asked, 'You still there?'

The next day at work, Aaron *did* seem to be making a beeline for Nancy. He even seemed to be making excuses to come to the kitchen and talk to her.

'See?' Rosie said, reversing through the swing door into the kitchen with a pile of dirty plates.

Gradually, Nancy relaxed into talking to Aaron without feeling embarrassed, and it turned out they had a lot in common. Apart from liking the same music, they'd both lost a grandparent they loved. Nancy found herself talking about Granny to Aaron on their first date – Bacardi and Coke in the Beau Nash pub, along the road from the hotel. It didn't feel like a date. It didn't feel awkward. It felt as if they were soulmates.

Aaron and Nancy became inseparable. They never ran out of conversation. They went out for meals together, they went for country rambles. They went to the seaside, and Nancy didn't even mind wearing her swimming costume in front of him. She became part of Aaron's family. He was an only child, and his mother said it was like having the daughter she'd always wanted. Aaron and Nancy went camping together in the summer, and in the winter, sat playing Scrabble and talking together in front of Aaron's living room fire, while the snow fluttered down outside. She was accepted, happy. Her self-esteem grew stronger and stronger. Anorexia was losing its grip.

Then she became pregnant.

There was no way Nancy could cope with having a baby. She still lived at home; she felt too immature to even think of becoming a mother, and Aaron was such a player, there's no way he'd want to settle down; have his life laid out like that. All he wanted to do was have a laugh, and go out to have fun. Plus, he was planning to go on tour with the band. He had high hopes for Shimma which didn't include being stuck at home changing nappies. Nancy suddenly felt that familiar gut-wrenching fear of losing control of her life again. She didn't dare tell Aaron. She didn't tell anyone, except Rosie.

Nancy couldn't go to Dr Pumphrey, so she looked in the *Yellow Pages* and found an abortion clinic in Brighton. It wasn't listed as that; it was euphemistically listed as a *Family Planning Clinic*, between *Faith Healers* and *Fancy Dress*. She made an appointment. It was going to cost £600, which was pretty much all the money she'd saved so far for a deposit for a flat. She caught the bus to Brighton, the Regency Route 29, thinking how all the other times she'd been on that bus, it had been to play the slot machines on the pier, swim in the sea, and eat fish and chips. She'd been dreading the counselling appointment, but when she arrived at the chic pistachio-green clinic, it turned out that the interview only involved two quick questions: 'Condom broke?' and, 'Are you sure you've thought this through?' That was it. They explained they'd perform the termination under a general anaesthetic. She was to arrive the following Monday morning at nine and she'd be ready to leave by four. Luckily, Monday was her day off.

On the day of the termination, Rosie came with her on the bus to the clinic, then left Nancy there while she went to the Sea Life Centre. To wangle the day off, Rosie had made an excuse about an emergency dental appointment. Nancy felt horrible making Rosie lie, and making her an accomplice to her secret.

The clinic was modern, slick, and the nurses calm and professional. It didn't feel real. When she was taken into the operating room, in her hospital gown printed with little bluebirds, she felt as if she was in a film. While they inserted a cannula, she winced, and looked at the picture on the ceiling. It was of horses, galloping through surf on a sunny beach. She was only aware of the anaesthetist's count down from ten to six, then found herself in a bright,

white room, in one of six hospital beds, with a huge
sanitary pad between her legs. A lady in a peach-coloured
nurse's uniform brought her a neatly-cut cheese and ham
sandwich and a cup of tea in a China cup and saucer. All
the other beds were taken with girls of a similar age. They
tried to smile at each other without actually getting into a
conversation. Nancy had to pee before they would let her
leave, so she drank as much of the water in the jug next to
her bed as she could, as fast as she could. She just wanted
it to be over with, and be gone. She was discharged with
a pack of birth control pills, and advice to, 'Make sure you
take them; you don't want this to happen again'.

Nancy had no need to take the pills. She couldn't face
Aaron, let alone have sex with him. She phoned him when
she got home, and made an excuse along the lines of, 'I still
love you, but I'm not *in* love with you'. It wasn't true. He
was the love of her life.

Nancy felt empty, both physically and emotionally. She
never wanted a relationship with a man again; not if this
could happen. She began to control her eating more
severely. No breakfast, a banana for lunch, a light salad for
tea. She started wearing over-sized, amorphous jumpers so
her mum wouldn't notice the shrinking.

Aaron and Nancy remained friends. She was still invited
to family meals with him; his mum's fiftieth; the silver
wedding anniversary. They even went on holiday together,
just as friends (no benefits). As the years passed, neither
Aaron nor Nancy met anyone new – no one that was more
than a one-night stand, anyway. Eventually they drifted
apart.

Nancy's brother, Tim, had married, and had two kids:
Josh and Bella. She couldn't help wondering what it might

be like to hold her own baby, what sex it might have been, what it might look like. It would be fifteen now. They'd be arguing about exam revision, or she'd be telling it not to try cigarettes. She didn't know whether it made it better or worse to think these things, but it made it difficult to babysit. Nancy didn't want to, but couldn't explain why, so she just got on with it. They were easy children to look after, anyway, and didn't argue as Tim and Nancy had done.

Then Nancy met Simon. He was an artist, and doing an excellent job of starving in a garret. Not a garret, exactly, but an attic bedsit in Grosvenor Road. Nancy was making good money by then, as a food and beverage manager in the hotel. She wasn't that interested in having a boyfriend, but there was something about Simon that got under her skin, and they soon became a couple. He was fragile. He said it was because of his childhood, but he didn't want to talk about it. As the relationship progressed, he began to lose his temper and shout at her. Not his fault, maybe, but not hers, either. He kept promising to get a job, but never did, or found jobs that only lasted a few days before he walked out. Nancy tried to make him happy; to love him better. She bought him a car, paid for a studio for him to paint in, paid for him to have weekends in Paris and Seville, to inspire him with his artwork. She was still controlling her weight, but sometimes it felt as if Simon were trying to control her, with some kind of hold over her that she couldn't shake off. He was an emotional – and financial – leech. She gave him everything, until she was both emotionally exhausted, and bankrupt.

It was the official receiver that showed her Simon was draining the life from her. He looked over his grey Formica desk, shuffled her bank statements and bankruptcy declaration together, and said, 'I shouldn't be saying this, really; it's not my place, but this man doesn't deserve you'. Nancy hadn't seen it herself, but someone else saying it, it made sense. She'd never be able to make Simon happy. That evening she packed her bags, drank a bottle and a half of Sauvignon Blanc, and drove away into the moonlight. She'd never driven drunk before, or since. It was a terrible, crazy thing to do. But she knew if she didn't leave at that moment, she would never leave at all. Nancy went back to her parents' to save up for a while, then found herself a new place to live: an upstairs flat in Secret Street.

A year or so later, Aaron found out that she'd dumped Simon, and came round to see Nancy, unannounced, just as Tim was there picking up Josh and Bella. They'd been sitting on the multicoloured ABC rug she brought out for them each time they came to play. They were building a farm with Lego, and playing with the wooden animals from their Noah's Ark. Aaron's eyes lit up when he saw them, and he sat down with them to play, making animal noises while Josh squeaked with delight and Bella clapped her hands. When Tim left, he could only prize the children away by promising them they'd be allowed to play with "Uncle Aaron" again soon. After they'd left, Aaron stayed sitting on the play rug while Nancy sat on the sofa, and he told her how he'd always wanted children, but the girlfriend he'd had while Nancy was with Simon had been unable to have them, and didn't want to adopt. Nancy could only sit in silence and nod. Her secret felt massive. She thought she might collapse beneath its weight. 'I'm such a cow', she thought. 'I'm a two-faced bitch.'

For a while, they slipped back into being the best friends they'd been before Nancy met Simon. The holidays

together, the family meals, the seaside trips, all started up
again. Aaron was always keen to be involved when Nancy
was babysitting Josh and Bella, and she knew she'd never
be able to tell him that she'd had the chance to have his
longed-for child, and thrown it away; taken his dream, and
trampled on it. What was more, as long as Aaron was
messing around with her, he wasn't out finding himself a
new woman to have a child with. Nancy decided that seeing
Aaron was just plain wrong. He wanted them to move
in together; she knew he did, but for the second time –
because of their secret unborn child – she ended her
relationship with the love of her life.

Nancy still lives alone. She keeps her flat spotless, like
a show home. Rosie says you'd almost think no one lives
there at all. Nancy has a new boyfriend, and he adores her.
He has his own grown-up children with his ex-wife. He
wants more from the relationship, but Nancy keeps it to one
date a week. They go out drinking, but he only stays over
occasionally. That suits her; she likes her own space.
Sometimes when he comes over she cooks them beautiful
meals, but then she doesn't eat the next day, to make up for
it. She feels so proud at the end of the day when she's stuck
to eating nothing. Today she's having a fat-free yogurt for
breakfast, a tomato Cuppa Soup for lunch, and a salad of
lettuce, tomato, and two lean slices – 160 calories-worth –
of ham for dinner. If things get out of hand, she looks at
that photo of herself in the garden with Mum: Mum,
Nancy, and anorexia. She keeps it in her wallet.

Darling, I think I'm about to disappear

Ten weeks before the Platinum Jubilee street party

Araminta has popped up to London to see the Royal Style in the Making exhibition at Kensington Palace. There isn't much Araminta doesn't know about royal style. For years she's devoured every piece of royal information she can find in expensive fashion magazines, gossipy cheap ones, royal-themed YouTube videos and websites, to find out what the Royals wear, and where they buy it. How better to elevate her class than to emulate the royal family? She's been looking forward to the exhibition for months, since she'd seen it announced in *Fashion Magazine*, but now here she is, tears running down her carefully made-up face, standing in front of a glass case containing the most famous wedding dress of all time: Princess Diana's. It's both the most exquisite and the saddest dress Araminta has ever seen. It stands erect and proud, but so very, very empty. It's as if Diana's ghost has lifted right out of it, taking all the poor girl's dreams of love to evaporate into the stale air above, and scutter about in this sealed glass display cabinet.

Diana had asked the designers, Elizabeth and David Emanuel, to make her a dress like a fairy tale princess's, and they'd risen magnificently to the occasion with this iconic creation with flounces, sequins, antique lace, and pearls. It pains Araminta to think the princess's dreams were doomed from the moment Diana was born.

Diana's parents were unhappy. Her father, Viscount Althorp, made it clear her very existence disappointed him because he had always wanted a son, and now here she was – his third daughter. Araminta knows what it's like to be a daughter to a father who wants a son. Diana's frequently tearful mother was sent for demeaning medical tests to find out why she kept failing to produce boys, even though that "fault" lay within her husband's, not her own chromosomes. Lady Althorp's husband divorced her, and her own mother – Diana's grandmother – testified against her at the child custody hearing. She was forced to abandon her children when Diana was ten. Diana hid the sadness inside her, constructing a gutsy, carefree persona, up for dares at boarding school, not giving a flying fig that she was a bit podgy. She left school to find a part-time job that she loved, helping to look after little children at a nursery, and happily worked as a cleaner, enjoying the satisfaction of taking a mess, and creating polished order in its place.

Then, there she was, a prisoner in a palace, engaged to her prince who was in love with, and having an affair with, his old polo chum, Camilla Parker Bowles. She felt a fool – a young girl who had sacrificed herself on a royal salver to be sliced and picked at by the Royals, and the Press, who called her "Shy Di". She believed with all her fragile heart that she was in love with Prince Charles, the man who would one day become King, but had stood next to him in front of the paparazzi and TV cameras only to hear him say, 'Whatever "in love" means'.

As soon as Diana was engaged to Charles, everything about her became wrong. Her self-esteem dissolved in her ignorance of the ways of royal life – when to curtsy, when to speak and when to be silent. Even the clothes she chose were deemed inappropriate. Always criticised and never praised, she felt she'd become a failure; a feeble freak. She couldn't even escape into the real world outside the palace on her own. Araminta pictures Diana venturing out without her bodyguard on a little jaunt to the shop to buy wine gums, only to find herself surrounded by a pack of news photographers, baying for a story, jostling for a photo. Charles had now made it clear that even her body was wrong when he'd disapprovingly said she was chubby. Diana was sick of it. Sick of the stifling palace atmosphere, sick of her loneliness, and sick of herself.

As she uses the public loo, Araminta looks at the striking, colourful Diana-themed wallpaper, and thinks there's far too much of the stiff upper lip about this exhibition. Too much pretending the whole thing is something to celebrate, not the disaster it became. All the colourful Diana-themed wallpaper in the world couldn't paper over what everyone knew about the poor, heartbroken, princess. Araminta imagines Diana locking herself in the bathroom, kneeling on the cold, tiled floor in front of the white toilet, leaning over, poking two fingers down her throat, and feeling her abdomen judder and convulse, as up came a whole regurgitated steak and kidney pie, three dollops of creamed potato, mange tout, gravy, carrot, two glasses of Malvern water, two bowls of custard, followed by a puddle of bitter-tasting yellow bile. Araminta shudders, imagining Diana gag and spit the last few crumbs of pie crust that had stuck at the back of her throat, flush the toilet, and crumple onto the floor beneath the pedestal basin. She imagines Diana sob with shame, disgusted with herself for gorging that amount of food, disgusted with herself for vomiting it all back up. Then, when she could sob no more, she would have washed her face, patted it dry, and tried to force her mouth into a smile as she closed the bathroom door behind her. But later, the hollow, primitive hunger she would have felt was hers. Nobody had given it to her; she had created that hunger herself, and it filled that empty place in her heart.

At her first wedding dress fitting, Diana's waist measured twenty-nine inches. By the time of the wedding, it was twenty-three and a half. What must the Emanuels have thought? Famously, when she visited Expo '86 (the World Exposition on Transportation and Communication) in Vancouver, Diana was so weak from hunger, she fumbled for Charles's shoulder, said, 'Darling, I think I'm about to disappear', and slid down his side to the ground. Araminta thinks of Diana's favourite requiem – Verdi's – and imagines Diana's moods swing dramatically from the high plaintive pianissimo of *Christe, Eleison*, to the forbidding crashes of the bass drum in the fortissimo *Dies Irae*. Araminta pictures the trailing bouquet of white roses and lily of the valley wilt, shrivel, and turn to dust.

The doctors, therapists and psychiatrists gave Diana platitudes and pills; tried to tranquilize her as if she were a badly-behaved brood mare. But all the king's horses and all the king's men...

At least when she became pregnant, Diana was allowed to refuse the tablets for fear of them harming the rapidly growing foetus inside her that might one day become King or Queen. Araminta remembers her own body when she was pregnant, changing like an unstoppable juggernaut; her waistline ballooning until it disappeared, her uterus pushing up in her pelvis, shoving her intestines and stomach up against her diaphragm and lungs, down and onto her bladder; her breasts swelling, and tender.

Araminta washes her hands and leaves the public bathroom. She cheers herself up thinking about how things started to improve for Diana when she met Dr Maurice Lipsedge. He was different. He listened. He understood. He told Diana she could recover, gave her books to read about bulimia, gave her hope, and gave her back her self-esteem. Diana began to discover she could purge herself less frequently and, instead, begin to take in and retain both physical and emotional nourishment. She learned how to increase her inner strength with tai chi, massage, and Chinese medicine, which showed her how anxiety can affect the spleen and digestive system. She tried new vitamin supplements, detoxifying and nutritious diets. She discovered the benefits of aromatherapy. She came upon mind-opening ideas from astrologers, and beautiful words from philosophers, including Khalil Gibran, who wrote of eating and drinking, *Let it be an act of worship*. Araminta had a little book of his. It was hardback, and the lightest turquoise, with a matching ribbon and gilt-edged pages.

Araminta enters the little gift shop and remembers when Diana opened the new shopping centre, Royal Victoria Place, in Tunbridge Wells in 1992. The Princess had looked so smart in a royal blue suit with black lapels, and had smiled so warmly. Araminta remembers what Toby had thought, standing in his policeman's uniform outside, and wonders how false Diana's smile had been. She pictures Diana travelling there with a heavy heart, hoping to get it over with quickly and smoothly and get back to Kensington Palace to her palatial but cosy living room, where the public and paparazzi were safely locked out.

Walking through Kensington Gardens to Lancaster Gate Underground Station, further and further away from that ghostly dress with each step, Araminta thinks about how Diana discovered her inner strength sufficiently to confront Camilla Parker Bowles, and lay to rest the torment of being the "other woman". Diana's shoulderless, figure-hugging, short black "Revenge Dress" that she'd worn after Charles' public admission of adultery said much more than words. More importantly, the princess discovered the strength in helping others; championing charities that worked to help the homeless, and people suffering with cancer and aids. She was strong enough to argue for a good divorce settlement, and to negotiate a new role for herself as an ambassador for Britain. No more opening shopping centres. How superb Diana looked in those famous land mine campaign photos! A stunning and capable woman in a flak jacket and safety visor. She instructed her hairdresser to cut away the bulky eighties-style fringe that she used to peep out from, and sported a new, feisty hair style. She was no longer a fragile, wilting flower, but strong, and taking life and all its difficulties by the horns. A perfect example of a woman self-actualising; becoming the best person she possibly could.

As Araminta glides down the escalator towards the Central Line, she listens to the rhythmic clunking of the metal gears beneath her feet, and wonders what it would be like to see another version of herself, on the escalator across the dreary sloping tunnel, gliding up.

The Sins of the Father

32 Secret Street –
Aoife's Story

For as long as she could remember, he was not to be spoken of. Any questions Aoife had for her mammy – or any other member of the family – about her father were shut down completely. There was nothing to be told. Granny made it clear she didn't like Aoife. If Aoife ever did anything wrong, Granny would say, 'You're just like him', so knowing how everybody felt about him, it was quite a blow for Aoife to hear that. She didn't like Granny at all. Mammy's sister, Auntie Clara, was nice, but she lived across the water in England.

In their village – Portfergus – Aoife didn't really understand what fathers did, because they didn't seem to do anything. The female population was simply meant to breed, and none of their ideas of self, or what they wanted to do, were ever taken into account. The mothers did school

216

planning, meal planning, cleaning, cooking, organising holidays; everything. All the fellas seemed to do was cause lots of babies for all these poor unfortunate women.

You had to be careful of the fellas, too.

If you went to Aoife's school, St. Mary of the Immaculate Conception, you'd know the quickest way to the playing fields was along the back path between the school and the convent. It was there, between an old, craggy convent wall and a high wire fence that Mr Gillespie, the convent gardener, seemed to be waiting for her.

'Off to play hockey, is it, young lady?' he asked.

She didn't like the look of him; his mouth had a sort of twist where a smile should be. Still, it seemed impolite not to say, 'Yes, to play hockey'.

Aoife expected him to let her pass, but he stood in front of her, reached down, and caught her knee with one of his heavy, rough hands, then slid the other up inside her grey pleated school skirt. She froze as his hand approached her gym knickers, but then lurched away, nearly fell, but regained her balance and ran back the way she'd come.

Panting, she went straight to the headmaster's office. Mr Blake was a lovely man; one of the only headteachers around that wasn't keen on corporal punishment. He used to talk to the children first and listen to what they had to say before thinking of getting out the slipper. He had soft-grey curly hair, and, instead of a suit jacket, he wore a toffee-coloured wool cardigan with suede panels down the front. With her head down and eyes glued to the floor, Aoife blurted out what the gardener had done.

'I believe you', he said, and she lifted her face to look at him. He smiled, gently. She realised she'd been holding her breath, and let it out in a big puff of relief. Mr Blake picked up the phone, and called Aoife's mammy to come to the school.

Mammy did not believe her. 'You're making me sick to my stomach', she said. 'How could you make up such lies?'

'It's not lies', Aoife pleaded, but she could see from the look on Mammy's face that there was no point in saying any more.

Then there was her friend Theresa's piano teacher. While Theresa practised her scales, her hands moving deftly up and down the piano keys, the music teacher's hand would be creeping up the inside of Aoife's thigh. It didn't help that Mammy dressed her in Sixties super-short dresses that were wildly inappropriate for her youthful age. Not that her mini skirts excused his behaviour, but they certainly gave him easy access.

Aoife's friend Niamh's father was a stereotypical drunken Irishman. Aoife hit puberty and developed a C cup bust pretty early on. The first time she went for a sleepover at Niamh's, he came into the bedroom and, well... Aoife had to just pretend to be asleep. She never went back to that house. Mammy never twigged. She assumed that because she knew the family they must be alright.

Mary Maloney's mother came to school every Monday morning with a black eye. Aoife remembers waking up one morning to find Mary asleep in her bedroom with her. Mammy encouraged Mary's mother to go to a refuge, but she wouldn't leave her husband. Aoife guessed that was why they were never to speak of her father; he must have been violent towards Mammy, or maybe towards her. Perhaps they'd been in a refuge when she was a baby, and she'd forgotten. But Mammy used to say of men, 'They just up and leave', and she'd often say to Aoife, 'No one bothered with you', so maybe it wasn't even about violence. Maybe he just wasn't interested.

Mammy made no bones about her lack of interest in Aoife, and she was very handy with the wooden spoon. Aoife was always covered in bruises. Apart from that, she was left to her own devices. Aoife thinks Mammy would have palmed her off on someone else if she'd been able to find someone to take her on. Not only was love scarce; money was, too. If she outgrew her shoes, Aoife's feet would hurt and that was that. If she was lucky she'd get a decent pair of hand-me-downs. Once she got some blue leather sandals with a big brass buckle; they were grand.

Aoife was very fond of "fancy", and one Saturday she found a sheer red and black babydoll nightie at the Barnardo's charity shop in the High Street. She was eleven, but Mammy thought it was OK for her to buy it. The first time Aoife met a father that did something useful was when she was on a sleepover, wearing that babydoll nightie, and he said,

'Now don't worry, but that's not appropriate for you, darling', and went away and came back with one of his daughters' cotton nighties for her to wear.

Aoife didn't feel shamed; she felt cared for. She liked that man; he was decent. It had been a revelation to see him involved with the family, playing with the children, washing dishes after supper. She thought, 'Ah, so that's what fathers are supposed to do!'

Life wasn't all bad. Aoife used to love the Sunday Club after morning Mass. All the children would run around like Looney Toons, then they'd have a Sunday roast. It was only years later that she realised she went to Sunday Club because the nun assigned to the church had identified her as one of the poor children of the parish, in need of decent clothes and a good hot meal once a week. People would donate dresses for families who couldn't afford them, and Aoife was given the best communion dress ever. It had belonged to the mayor's daughter. It was bridal-looking, demure, full-length white satin and lace. She looked so fancy on that day! The neck was lace, the sleeves were lace and fluted, there was a big silk bow at the back, and it came with gloves and a veil. She was a little bride of God. She can picture the photo now, with her long, black curly hair beneath the veil, and her blue, smiling eyes.

After lunch, they'd play board games, or play music and practise their Irish dancing. The best thing, though, was art; big sheets of cream-coloured sugar paper, squeezy bottles of red, blue, and yellow paint, and jam jars with wooden-handled paint brushes just begging to be picked up and sploshed about. They gave Aoife a man's shirt with the collar cut off to wear back to front for an apron. That's where her love of art began. At school they had to draw boring things, like hands, and bowls of fruit, but at Sunday Club she could swing the brush around the paper with big, sweeping splashes of paint she could mix to any colour of the rainbow. The nuns entered two of her paintings in competitions, and Aoife won, twice. There was a picture of her in the *Portfergus Gazette* with the mayor, holding her painting in one hand and her medal in the other, beaming at the camera. The painting was of a house on fire, with flames in shades of scarlet, yellow and tangerine, and a fire engine hosing on sapphire, cyan and aquamarine water. The mayor said lovely things to her. She didn't mention that she'd worn his daughter's dress for her communion, but she tried to smile at him as much as possible, to silently thank him for donating it.

Aoife and Mammy had to go into town to buy the *Gazette*, even though they sold it at the village shop down the road from their house; the shop that was next to a strange little terrace of blank-faced houses, so different from the detached Irish bungalows she was used to. They never went in that shop. When they reached ,the terrace, they always crossed to the other side of the road to pass it. When Mammy wasn't looking, Aoife would stare at the shop, with its newspaper sandwich board that announced important local headlines, such as, *Local councillor defends doughnut budget*, or *Man Bites Dog!* She'd look at the houses, and the green in front where daffodils grew in the spring, and pink and blue foxgloves in summer. She never asked Mammy why they couldn't go in the shop. She knew by the way Mammy put her head down and bit her lower lip as they passed that it was safer not to.

Aoife was the only child at school that didn't have a pa. Each year on Father's Day when they had to make cards, she was excused, and sent to the library to read. That was fine, she didn't mind; she loved books, always has. The first time she started to think something was very wrong was in secondary school, when they had a religious education assessment which involved asking your parents about their relationship. So she went home and asked Mammy about it, and Mammy burst into tears and then refused to talk to her for two whole days.

Aoife did alright at school, and ended up with A levels in English, biology, and art. She got 'A' for art, and left Ireland to go to art college across the water in England. Afterwards she trained as an art therapist. She met her husband, Pete, at the post-grad college. She fell pregnant a little earlier than they'd planned, and, being a good Catholic, that meant they had to be married. And *that* meant Aoife needed a birth certificate.

She didn't dare ask Mammy; she forked out to get a new one from the General Registry Office. Aoife didn't know her father's name, but there can't have been many girls called Aoife born in Portfergus on her birth date. When the certificate arrived, she found herself staring at the brown envelope with its harp franking mark for a good half hour before she plucked up the courage to open it.

Her father's name was... her father's name *is*, John Gerald O'Neill. She thought that sounded quite nice. When she saw his occupation, a warm tingle spread from her head all the way down to her toes: *Artist*. He was a good man; he must be. She Googled him immediately, typing *John Gerald O'Neill artist*, and found a couple of records of paintings he'd had exhibited in a gallery in Kilkenny, but no pictures of them, and nothing at all after the time she was born. So then she searched his name and *Portfergus*.

There it was; the newspaper headline – *Local Man Convicted of Rape*. Staring back at her from the photo was a mugshot of a man with the same curly black hair as hers, the same blue eyes, the same small mouth, and wide cheekbones.

There were other news reports. All sexual assaults on women he knew. Initially one woman came forward when Mammy was pregnant, and then several others. He was fond of giving women lifts and assaulting them in his car.

Aoife needed to talk to someone, and the only person was Mammy's sister, Auntie Clara. There was some Courvoisier brandy left from Christmas, and she poured herself a large one and gulped it down in front of the computer screen, staring at that photo. Then she picked up the phone.

'Auntie Clara, it's Aoife.'

'What is it, luvvy?' Clara asked.

'I'm looking at a photo of my father in the *Portfergus Gazette*.'

'Ah', she said, 'I'm sorry, my darling'.

Auntie Clara explained to Aoife that the rape was of a local woman he'd given a lift to. He was sentenced to a minimum of eight years. Aoife had to check that she wasn't born as a result of a rape, and Auntie Clara said, 'No, John was good to your mammy; they were very much in love. But it wasn't safe for her in the village, and Mammy had to leave for a while. I know she's hard on you, but it might help to know what she went through. They spat in your pram, Aoife – the villagers – they spat in your pram'.

For weeks, Aoife could think of nothing else. She ruminated over whether it would have been worse if her father had raped her mother and she'd been born of that rape. She knew it was stupid, but couldn't stop herself thinking it. She wondered why Mammy hadn't gone over the water for an abortion. She wondered if Mammy hated her because she looked so much like him. Granny was right, at least in that respect, she *was* like him.

Aoife needed to meet him, and his family. She needed to know more about the other half of her. She knew absolutely nothing about them, and – especially being pregnant – she wanted to know more. Was there a violent gene that her baby might inherit? Or an illness? Auntie Clara told her that her father was still living in the same house he'd been in when he met her mother. Aoife asked her where. It was in the same road as the forbidden corner shop.

Four weeks later and Pete and Aoife were driving down that road, counting the numbers, looking for No. 6. Then Pete said, 'That has *got* to be a relative'.

The woman outside her front door looked exactly like Aoife, just a bit taller. She was her father's sister; Auntie May, and the house was one of the strange little terraces with the flowers outside, next to the shop. Aoife wound down the window, Pete slowed down, and Aoife called across to the woman,

'I'm looking for John O'Neill'.

The woman called back, 'Then you must be Aoife'.

She invited them in, and they sat on the sofa with a big family of people that all – in one way or another – looked like Aoife. Her new auntie said,

'We'd heard you were coming; we thought you'd come yesterday'.

Aoife replied, 'No I had to go and lie down; I was sick as a dog on the ferry'.

She didn't say she was pregnant. That was Pete's and her personal business, and somehow it didn't feel right to tell them. They were all lovely, though; so welcoming. Her father was there. He was out of prison at that point. It turned out he had five brothers and sisters. It was a warm, caring family. All Irish families have a rogues' gallery of photos, and in there was one of Aoife aged about ten in a pink and orange candy-striped mini dress; that communion photo in the mayor's daughter's dress; a school photo, with her hair in bunches and wearing a grey cardigan and red and black striped tie; her photo from the school graduation gala, in a long blue satin gown that her auntie had bought her, to bring out the colour of her eyes. Then nothing. She realised that the only way she could be in that rogues' gallery was if someone from her side of the family had been providing them with photos, and it must have been Mammy's father. The photos had stopped abruptly about six years previously, which is when he'd died.

Auntie May told her afterwards that when Aoife phoned up and arranged the visit, she'd said to Aoife's father, 'You have to tell her what happened, otherwise you'll never see her again. Because she's made up her mind she wants to see you, you must be honest'.

Aoife had only been there half an hour, when he decided it was time to make his revelation, and said,

'Let's go for a walk'.

She thought, 'Knowing what I know now, I don't really want to be alone with you, unless we're in a public place'. So she said, 'We can walk up the main road; there's a shop up there at the Esso petrol station, and we can buy some chocolate'.

So they walked; him in his grey anorak, and Aoife in her emerald green duffle, beyond the terrace and onto the grass verge, past low, sprawling detached houses with garages and big gardens with kids' football goals and bicycles, past the self-catering bungalows and the riding stables, past the primary school with children in red jumpers running and laughing in the playground, until they came to the Esso. And all the time Aoife was thinking, 'I am walking with my father'. And all the time, he was telling her lies.

He said there had been women who'd misunderstood his intentions, and become upset. 'I was accused of sexual impropriety...' he began.

Because she was on the main road, with potential witnesses everywhere, Aoife was brave enough to stand up to him. 'You raped her!' she said. 'It wasn't sexual impropriety. Sexual impropriety is maybe patting her on the backside, or touching her knee, or maybe even groping her boob. What you did was completely different.'

He didn't reply. Silently, they walked into the garage shop, and at the shelf with the chocolate bars, simultaneously reached for a bar of Cadbury's Fruit & Nut.

Aoife went away from that meeting and she's never been back. She *has* since spoken to Auntie May, she's friends with her on Facebook, and they chat on Messenger. Aoife's told her that her father hadn't been particularly honest with her and it didn't feel that she gelled with him; that she would love to be in contact with them as a family, but not him. She knows that makes life difficult for them, because they're a big cohesive family, they all love each other, and they're supportive of her father, but she doesn't want anything to do with him. So they have this uneasy alliance now where they're in contact on Facebook, but they shouldn't be. Aoife sees photos of big family gatherings – *her* family – with aunties, uncles, grandparents, and children. Everyone's there except her.

As Aoife grew older and had her own children, she made a conscious decision that her father wouldn't know their names, that he'd never see photos, and she's asked Auntie May not to pass any information about them on. Aoife said that it would be up to them if the family wish to contact her, but she asked her to respect her own decision that she doesn't want him to see her children growing up. She doesn't trust someone that can't be open with her. There's so much unknown, and he could be a danger to them. Aoife doesn't know if that's true or not; it could be completely unfounded, but she won't take that risk.

She's always been hypervigilant over her children, about who babysat them, who they were in contact with. If she didn't get the right vibe about them, they didn't even go for afternoon tea. She's talked to her children about touching and what's acceptable, and what isn't. She said, 'These are your bits and pieces and nobody has the right to touch them. At all'.

The hypervigilance can be useful, though. The summer before last, her daughter was having tennis lessons, and Aoife saw the way the tennis coach was looking at her; at the curves of her breasts and her thighs beneath her tennis dress. The hair stood up on the back of Aoife's neck.

He must have seen her noticing, because afterwards he said to her, 'Your daughter has lovely eyes'. And she thought, 'It's not her eyes you're looking at'.

Back home, she said to Pete, 'She's not going back to that tennis school'.

Four weeks later, the coach was arrested for sexual assaults on children. He's in prison now.

At one point Aoife wondered, as an adult, were all those assaults on her as a little girl because they knew about her history – her father's history – and thought she was fair game? She doesn't know. More likely than not, they were just opportunists. She thinks a lot of her anxiety and trauma-based responses as an adult are because she couldn't trust adults at all, particularly male ones, and that was reinforced by finding out about her father when she got a bit older. It was hard with Pete at times, for their marriage; Aoife had lots of emotional armour. She sometimes wonders what life would have been like with a supportive mother, and a father who was respected in the community, or simply with a father worthy of being called Pa.

Aoife's always loved children. She's the first to rush over to smile and coo when a colleague comes into the office from maternity leave with their new baby. She's been an art therapist for years, but only recently started working with children, as if she had to make peace with her past before she could give herself permission to do that.

Aoife used to subscribe to Mammy's view of men, but not now. There are good, kind men who aren't sex offenders and aren't even eejits, like that nice pa with the nightie, and Mr Blake at school, and her Pete. Most men – most people – are just doing the best they can in the circumstances they find themselves. She tries not to let her childhood – her background – taint her any more. Children are naturally egocentric, so until she grew older, Aoife used to assume that all those sexual assaults were her fault. Now she realises that adults make their own choices, and children aren't responsible for what happens to them. She can leave all that stuff where it is.

Aoife still considers herself Irish. She'll always identify as Irish. She misses the softness of the rain and the green scent it brings once the showers have stopped. She misses the smell of turf burning in the big old Aga in the kitchen. She misses the soda bread, baked fresh every morning at Brennan's, and how you can tell from the strong, mouthwatering fragrance of it which houses have had a delivery as you walk down the road in the morning. But since Aoife's had children, she's not been back to Ireland at all. She doesn't know if it's just that it doesn't feel safe, or doesn't feel nice, or she feels a bit aggrieved knowing more now than she did as a child about how people treated her.

She knows you're supposed to reclaim the places you associate with bad memories; make new memories; laugh in the places you used to cry. She might go back home to Ireland and do that one day. Might.

The Meeting

Six weeks before the Platinum Jubilee Party

Araminta had popped to Hooper's for some royal-themed serviettes for that afternoon's meeting. She had a coffee in the café upstairs, wishing she'd been able to pluck up the courage to ask Denise from next door to come with her. Afterwards, she lingered in the small bedding section next to the restaurant entrance. There was a display bed made up with a luxurious duvet cover and matching pillowcases in a shades of olive and gold, decorated with hand-painted peonies and camellias. £240.00. She might come back another day and put it on her credit card. While she was looking at the bedlinen there were two other women choosing cushions; typical private school graduates, like Beatrice. You could tell them a mile off. They had long hair, expensively streaked with highlights and lowlights, and they all somehow dressed the same. Each carried their head with the chin slightly lifted, as if they were deliberately avoiding seeing anything beneath them. At weekends, you'd see them strutting in the High Street or the Pantiles, with their husbands wearing quilted Barbour jackets and looking slightly lost. These two seemed to be vying with each other for who could speak in the most affected way; not quite like the Queen, but almost. As they chatted to each other, one of them picked up a cushion and looked at it with a sort of haughty discernment. 'Of course the only things we thought about at school were boys and skiing trips', she shrilled. Araminta wondered were these the sort of women she'd spent her life trying to copy. She'd never been on a skiing trip, and she'd never look effortlessly posh like they do. She didn't even like them.

As she reached the handbag section, she remembered there was a yellow Mulberry handbag that had been calling to her for several weeks now. £1040. But Mulberry, though! She knew where the bag was, picked it up, stroked it, and took it to the counter to pay.

'What an excellent choice', said the woman behind the till. 'I'd like this one myself.' The shop assistant was impeccably dressed, with a silk scarf around her neck, a sweater that looked like cashmere, and tailored grey wool trousers. *Jane*, her staff badge said.

'Yes, hwhat a cheery colour!' Araminta enthused, wondering why a woman who could afford silk and cashmere was working in a shop; whether Jane could afford a Mulberry handbag of her own, and feeling a little sorry for her. As Jane slid the bag into its dust cover and pulled out sheets of tissue paper from beneath the counter, Araminta slotted her Barclaycard into the card machine, and entered her PIN.

CARD DECLINED, it said.

'Perhaps you put in the wrong PIN?' said Jane, helpfully. Araminta was sure she hadn't, but tried again.

CARD DECLINED, insisted the card reader. A chill spread through Araminta's body.

'Do you have another card?'

Araminta felt as if the handbags on the shelves behind her were sniggering. It occurred to her that Jane the shop assistant looked a bit like Mean Jean from school. 'I'll try my Access', she heard herself say. Her Access card was declined, too. An expression of disdain crept across Jane's face.

'Perhaps your current account?'

Araminta knew there was only about £30 left in there.

'I so rarely use it, I can't remember the PIN number', she lied.

'Shall I keep the bag aside for you to return later with an alternative method of payment?'

'Who feels sorry for whom now?' Araminta thought, and replied, 'Yes, please, that would be lovely of you', knowing she wouldn't come back and buy it at all, and suspecting Jane knew it, too.

In the car park, as Araminta put her current account card in the machine to pay, she remembered the pile of unopened letters in her hall cupboard, with words like *FINAL DEMAND* on some of them in black, others in red. She thought of the hire costs for the Jubilee street party trestle tables, the gazebos, the table linen, the silver napkin rings, piling up in her imagination as if building a towering bonfire. The final party-planning meeting was in two hours' time. What in God's name was she going to do?

***

'It's charming, isn't it? I couldn't resist it.' Araminta rewinds the musical Platinum Jubilee-themed biscuit tin. It plinks the National Anthem, out of tune and out of time, as gaily painted characters – a Beefeater, a Chelsea Pensioner, a Scottish piper – parade unsteadily around the sides of the tin, blowing bugles, waving flags.

'Marks and Spencer.' Araminta picks it up, removes the lid, and offers the shortbread shapes inside to Aslan, Nancy, Aoife, Toby, Olivia from No. 19, and Stephen from The Otter, who are all seated on her yellow Knowle sofas.

'I love how horribly out of tune it is!' says Aoife.

'That's part of its charm', says Nancy. She picks the tin up from where Araminta has put it down on the coffee table, and winds it up again.

'I wasn't at the first meeting', says Stephen, 'do I need to be brought up to speed?'

They wait for Araminta to speak, but she doesn't.

Plink, plinkety-plink... goes the biscuit tin.

'We need more Earl Grey', says Araminta, and takes a still-half-full teapot to the kitchen.

As Araminta stands in the kitchen next to the kettle and waits for it to boil, there are three loud knocks on the door. Aslan wonders why whoever it is doesn't use the chiming doorbell.

'That'll be Jed', calls Araminta from the kitchen. 'Aslan, could you get it, please?'

Aslan swings open the front door to two men; a tall thin one in a long, black overcoat, and a short, wide one in a black puffer jacket.

'Is Mrs Cavendish here?' asks the tall man, with an air of seriousness that makes Aslan wonder whether he should invite them in or not.

'There are some people here for you', he calls to Araminta.

As she approaches the door, the shorter man holds out a brown envelope, and Araminta takes it, as he says,

'We have been appointed by the courts on behalf of your creditors to remove goods to the value of one thousand, eight hundred and fifty-one pounds and eighty-six pence'.

At first it doesn't register. Then Araminta's legs seem to crumple beneath her and she falls slowly to her knees, where she huddles with her hands in front of her face.

'There must be some mistake', says Aslan. He always assumed Araminta was a wealthy widow.

'No mistake, sir', says the shorter man, 'Mrs Cavendish is well aware of the situation. Several attempts have been made to communicate with her'.

The bailiffs swan past Aslan and Araminta to the living room, where they begin to eye up the Royal Doulton figurines crowding the mantelpiece.

'I'll fetch some packing cases from the van', says the tall one, and walks back towards the front door.

'Wait', says Aslan, 'you can't do this to a poor elderly widow'.

'I'm afraid Mrs Cavendish has consistently ignored written warnings over a period of nine months. We are left with no other option.'

'How much do you need, now, to go away and leave her alone?'

'One thousand, eight hundred and...'

'The whole amount?'

'Yes, sir.'

'Come with me. I only live four houses down. I will write a cheque', says Aslan.

The men seem happy with this, and follow Aslan out of the door.

'Aslan mustn't do that; it's not right', wails Araminta, as Beatrice and Aoife gently encourage her to her feet, steer her to a sofa, and sit her down. Beatrice sits next to her as Araminta begins to cry, and gently pats Araminta's back.

Aoife pours a cup of tea, adds three sugar lumps and says, 'Sugar for shocks', as she stirs.

Nancy and Toby don't know what to say, and try to look as sympathetic as possible.

'He can't do that! It's too much', sobs Araminta, 'and I'm not even a widow'.

'Oh!' says Beatrice, 'I thought, you know, your "dear departed Frederick"'.

'He departed, but not this life; just his life with me. I loved him, desperately, but I wasn't enough for him.'

Toby looks across and smiles at Araminta encouragingly.

'Marriages are difficult. There are always two sides to the story', he says.

'Yes', says Aoife, 'fault – if indeed there is any – is rarely ever only on one side'.

Aslan rings the doorbell, and Stephen lets him in, as well as Jed, who's walking up the path towards the house just behind Aslan.

'I couldn't let them treat you like that', says Aslan to Araminta, as he sits down across the room from her. 'They have gone now.'

'Sorry I'm late', says Jed, 'I couldn't miss therapy. Who's gone now?'

'The bailiffs', says Toby. Jed looks puzzled.

'Aslan has just paid my debt', explains Araminta, 'and it was far too much for him to pay, and I can't pay him back'. Araminta dries her eyes on one of her napkins. 'I took out one of those equity release things, to get the roof replaced, and to go and see Jenny in Australia. Then the monthly payments were a little difficult to make, so I took out a credit card to keep me going, and...'

'We'll work something out', says Aslan, 'I am an accountant, after all. And I couldn't let them treat a poor elderly widow like that'.

'She's not a widow!' chorus Toby and Beatrice.

'I'm just so embarrassed; I've lied to you all.'

'You didn't really lie', says Nancy.

'I let you believe I'm a widow.'

'Perhaps we should leave, get out of your hair?' asks Stephen.

'No, please stay. I want to tell you everything. If I don't clear the air now, I'll be too embarrassed to face any of you ever again. I'm not a widow; I'm a liar! A pathetic little liar.' She changes her accent to West Country. 'And I'm not even called Araminta; my real name's Ivy Brown. I wanted to better myself, so I done elocution lessons, and I changed my name, to sound posh. And my 'usband; 'e left me because he's gay.'

'I changed my voice, too', says Stephen, helpfully, 'not because I wanted to better myself; just because I wanted the bullying to stop. At school'. Stephen continues in a hammy Australian accent. 'I should sound like this: Goo'day, cobbers, I hope you're all having a bonzer time this arvo!'

The others smile.

'I live a lie, too', says Nancy, quietly. 'You won't tell anyone else, though, will you?'

'Of course not', says Araminta, 'if you're sure you want to tell us'.

'I never eat any of my cakes.'

The others look puzzled.

'I'm anorexic.'

'Oh, you poor lamb', says Beatrice, 'so you wear the big jumpers because you're too thin, not too fat?'

'Yes. But it's my private business; I shouldn't have told you really. I just get sick of people going on about me being slim, and my jumpers and tunics.'

'It must be hard to keep that all to yourself', says Aoife, 'and now that we know, you won't be alone with it any more'.

'I'm so sorry I was praising you for being slim', says Beatrice, thoughtfully.

'You weren't to know', says Nancy. She won't tell them about the termination. Some secrets can never be told.

'Well, I have a secret, too', announces Beatrice. 'I know you all think I'm a wealthy middle-class lady and live a perfect life, but my husband died of alcoholism, and my son, well, it's not my story to tell, but he's had his difficulties, too.'

'Addiction affects everyone – rich or poor', says Jed.

'That must have been so hard for you', says Aoife.

The others nod.

'This is very sad', says Aslan.

'George's family left me very well provided for, of course', adds Beatrice. She wasn't sure she felt as sorry for Araminta as the others seemed to. She didn't have a ridiculously enormous collection of China and porcelain, neither did she go in for those designer handbags she'd seen Araminta carrying, as if Araminta thought she was some kind of social media influencer. Beatrice always put a little by each month in case of emergencies. And she really could not abide liars. Maybe, though, Araminta's situation was a case of a difficult childhood that had left her unable to plan and organise. Or maybe that roof unexpectedly cost far more than she could afford on her pension. Perhaps, thought Beatrice, she should feel more compassion.

'Now, what can I tell you? I feel a bit left out if I don't tell you a secret', says Aoife. 'Right, I'm going to tell you.' She takes a deep breath. 'My father was a rapist! How about that, then?' She smiles. 'I don't know why I'm smiling', she adds, thoughtfully.

'Wow!' says Nancy.

Olivia says nothing. She can't give away her daughter Kizzy's secret. As Beatrice said about Hugo, that secret wasn't Olivia's to tell.

Jed thinks of his childhood. It was brutal. It would be too upsetting for them to hear, so he says, 'What we're doing right now is overcoming stigma. The sociologist, Erving Goffman, called stigma "spoiled identity". Not only does stigma keep us in our place – maintain the status quo – but we internalise it and stigmatise ourselves by keeping these secrets. I learned this stuff when I did my degree'. Jed notices Stephen looking surprised. 'You don't expect someone who's been homeless and is living in a rehab to have a degree, do you?'

'Well, no, I suppose...' says Stephen, awkwardly.

'Don't feel bad about it', says Jed, 'that's stigma, reinforcing the hierarchy with the elite at the top, telling us who should be in charge'.

'With the Royal Family at the top?' says Nancy.

'Yes', says Jed, 'which is why we don't like it if one of them lets us down by being imperfect; it challenges the status quo'.

'Well done us; challenging the status quo by swapping secrets', says Araminta.

'But what has been said in this room stays in this room, yes?' says Toby.

The others say 'Yes', or 'Of course'.

Aslan wonders if he dare tell them he was brought to England via people smugglers, but decides it's too much of a risk. He knows when it comes to seeking asylum, people are confused about what's legal and what isn't, and he doesn't want it getting round the community, and maybe damaging the reputation of the accountancy business, all for nothing. He smiles to himself as his mind flits joyfully back to that moment when the goods truck door rattled open, and he saw the British Transport Police.

'Come on, let's sort out this party', says Aoife.

'But I can't afford the trestle tables, or the gazebos – not a sausage. Literally not even a tiny little cocktail sausage', says Araminta.

'Everyone will muck in', says Aoife. 'I'll get the kids who live in the street to make bunting, we can all bring our own food and drink, and most people have garden tables and chairs.'

'You can buy cheap and cheerful jubilee tablecloths in Aldi', says Beatrice.

Araminta looks surprised.

Beatrice notices her expression. She knows Araminta has her groceries delivered by Ocado once a week. 'Thrift, darling, thrift! My family is "old money"; we were brought up to save the pennies where we can. I mean, why pay more?'

'I've been doing posh all wrong', says Araminta, wistfully thinking of how much joy a green and gold Lyles' Golden Syrup tin brings her compared to a plain supermarket plastic bottle.

'Maybe I could give you some budgeting tips?' suggests Beatrice.

Aoife frowns. She thinks that's a little patronising, but Araminta nods enthusiastically.

'And Aldi do Angel Slices as good as Mr Kipling's, but half the price', says Toby.

'And we don't need gazebos, says Nancy. 'If it rains we can all sit under umbrellas and laugh about it.'

'Or wear our Rain-mate bonnets', says Araminta, 'if you're old enough to remember what they are'.

'Oh, God, yes, Rain-mates! Those ridiculous see-through plastic things?' says Nancy.

'That's the ones', says Araminta.

'I wonder if they come in a Union Jack design?' says Aoife, with a snorty giggle.

'I have no idea what you are talking about', says Aslan, smiling. 'Come on, more tea, more biscuits, and we'll draft that letter to everyone in Secret Street, so they know what is happening'.

'You know – all these secrets; all these things that have happened to us?' says Araminta. 'Well, when we had all the trouble with Fred, the girls and I used to say, "At least we don't live the Lily life."'

'What is the Lily Life?' asks Aslan.

The others listen intently as Araminta replies.

'Lily was a girl we knew, who grew up in a perfect family: happy parents, both senior nurses, two children; a boy, and a girl. Every year they used to have one room in their house professionally decorated, and every Summer they went to Tenerife for a fortnight, every Christmas to Austria. Lily did well at school, grew up and became a nurse like her parents, married a doctor, settled down and had two kids, and went on holiday every Summer and Christmas. Bought a nice three-bedroomed semi, had one room decorated each...'

'Boring!' says Aslan. He laughs. 'Yes, I would rather this, than the Lily life.'

The others smile and nod in agreement.

'Poor Lily', says Toby, grinning. 'Come on now, Araminta; put the kettle on.'

'Call me Ivy!'

'Your legal name is Araminta, though, surely?' says Stephen.

'Yes, and I went back to Cavendish after the divorce. But I wanna have a go at being Ivy again, while I still have the years to do it.'

'Well, the thing is...' Stephen fidgeted in his seat a little. 'Since we're being honest – we all call you "Minty"'.

'Behind my back?' asks Araminta.

'Well, yes, but in an affectionate way', says Olivia.

Araminta thinks for a moment. They've all been laughing at her, but she deserves it.

'"Minty" still somehow sounds awfully posh!' says Olivia.

Araminta finds herself bursting into a fit of giggles. The others laugh, too.

'Alright, then. I'm going to change my name back to Ivy Brown by deed poll. It will be symbolic.'

'So you want for us to call you Ivy?' says Aslan.

'If that's alright? If it isn't too much of a faff?'

'Ivy it is!' says Aoife. 'I love this so much; the symbolic change to signify becoming your true, authentic self.'

'Ivy it is, then!' says Toby.

"Ivy put the kettle on", sings Jed, to the tune of Polly Put the Kettle On.

'Lovely voice', says Olivia.

Stephen taps his teacup loudly with a spoon, and raises it.

'I propose a toast', he announces, 'To Ivy!'

The others raise their cups, and chorus,

'To Ivy!'

19 Secret Street – Olivia

A fortnight before the Platinum Jubilee Party

Olivia and Araminta-now-Ivy are sitting at the bar in The Otter, chatting to Stephen. They're on the subject of blind dates. It started because there's a couple in the corner who they're guessing hadn't known each other before they arrived. The woman had come in hesitantly, and looked around the pub – presumably for a man sitting on his own – before approaching him, smiling politely, and saying, 'Hello, how lovely to meet you'.

'Could be a business meeting', suggests Olivia.

'No, there's no paperwork', says Ivy.

'Nor laptop', says Stephen.

'And she looks nervous', adds Olivia.

'I had one recently', says Ivy. The others look surprised.

'A blind date?' asks Stephen.

'Yes, I know; at my age! My daughter talked me into it.'

'How did it go?' asks Olivia.

'It didn't go well at all. He turned up in two-tone denim ankle swingers and white socks.'

'Oh my God!' laughs Olivia.

'Is that bad?' asks Stephen.

'Yes!' chorus the women.

'Hey, want to hear about my blind dates?' says Olivia.

'Dates, plural?' says Stephen.

'Tell all!' says Ivy, nodding enthusiastically.

'Well, this was about twenty years ago, when dating websites were new and still catered for wholesome friendships, as in, *Three good lads wanted to join climbers for the Three Peaks Challenge*, or, *Buddy to join me getting fit for the London Marathon*. I wanted something wholesome, too, I thought. Someone to become friends with first, then maybe lovers, and then maybe something more permanent.

The first guy I risked was called Alan and was from Crowborough...'

Ivy looks confused.

'Yes', says Olivia, 'I used to date men. None of my relationships worked, but then Fran got in touch with me via Twitter. She was my best friend at school. We all knew she was gay...'

'But you didn't know you were?'

'Well, I didn't think I fancied her, just knew that I loved her company. I loved everything about her, really. Anyway, yes, she found me on Twitter when I was pregnant with Kizzy. She was moving down here from London to work in Sevenoaks, and I suggested she stay with me while she looked for somewhere to live. It was funny; she started off on the sofa, then we slept together in my double bed with pillows between us for two whole weeks before we actually touched each other.'

Ivy thinks that if she were otherwise inclined, she would fancy Olivia herself. Liv has the cutest body, which always looks amazing in jeans (which Liv's wearing now, with a sky-blue fluffy fleece), and she has a gorgeous brown bob that frames her smiling face, with freckles either side of her slightly upturned nose, which reminds Ivy of the darling little wooden puppets she'd bought Jenny and Becky when they went on a family holiday to Amsterdam.

'So it was difficult to admit you were gay… sorry, bi?' says Stephen.

'It wasn't so much about coming out as bi; we were just shy, sexually, I think. It was wonderful; I almost felt an electric shock if my hand happened to brush past hers.'

'So, hang on a minute…' says Ivy.

The others wait patiently for her to collect her thoughts.

'Here's the thing: If you had been with a man when you realised you were in love with Fran, would he have felt you leaving him for a woman was a sort of…' she tries to find the right words, '…affront to his masculinity?'

'Oh. How would I know? Maybe?' says Olivia.

'What do you think, Stephen?' says Ivy. 'If your wife had left you for a woman, would it have made you feel…'

'Less of a man, you mean?' says Stephen.

'Yes.' Ivy nods.

'Maybe… probably', says Stephen.

'The thing is', says Ivy, 'that when Fred left me for a man, I felt I was a complete failure; not just as a wife, but as a woman'.

'But', says Olivia, 'that's flawed logic. I stopped dating men because I met the love of my life, who happened to be a woman, not because I'd stopped fancying men. I used to have some great sex with men!'

Stephen's blushing. He wishes he wasn't so repressed, and that he found these things easy to talk about.

Ivy takes a sharp, loud, intake of breath. 'I've just realised something.' She presses her hand over her mouth momentarily as the others wait for her to continue. 'My father wanted me to be a boy. He would frequently, and merrily, tell me this, with no qualms whatsoever. So maybe... maybe I took it so hard when Fred left me for a man because I felt...'

'That in not being a man, you were failing Fred?' suggests Stephen.

'That once again, you were denied love, because you weren't a boy; a man?' says Olivia.

'Yes', exclaims Araminta, 'exactly that!'

'This is like a therapy session', says Stephen.

They all smile.

'If only people could talk openly about these things, we wouldn't all need therapy all the effing time', says Olivia.

'It's that stigma again', says Stephen, 'dividing and conquering; keeping the "normals" as the elite; making us feel shame'. He sighs. 'I used to feel ashamed about being adopted.'

'That's so sad', says Ivy. 'It had nothing to do with you; the fact that you were put up for adoption. It can't possibly be a flaw in your character.'

'But still, I always felt second best.'

As he speaks, he looks suddenly broken. Olivia and Ivy see a whole new side to this gregarious pub landlord, who deals with obstreperous punters effortlessly, who had made a success of his business.

'You were going to tell us about your blind dates, Olivia', he says, in a jolly voice, as if his new tone can clear the air of his sadness.

'Call me Liv', she says. 'Right. Yes, where were we?'

'The man from Crowborough.'

'Yes, Alan. We met at the Crowborough Cross pub, where he regaled me for an hour with his love of model railways. I couldn't get a word in edgeways. Eventually I pretended I had a headache. It was pathetic of me, but it was the only thing I could think of quickly in my desperation. The next day, he sent several messages via the app suggesting, then begging for, another date, ignoring my subtle put-downs, and in the end I had to blatantly tell him, "I'm sorry, I didn't feel we gelled, so I don't want another date with you." Then he called me a prick-tease and flounced off in a huff.'

'What, in his socks and sandals?' says Ivy.

'Actually, yes', laughs Olivia. 'Next was a judge. A High Court Judge.'

'Oo!' exclaims Ivy.

'I know! My mother was very excited. Actually, it was between the judge and Phil, who ran a dry cleaning business. The judge – whose name, Kevin, was somehow unexpected for his career – lived in a giant detached house in Surrey, and suggested a date at a wine bar called The Lemon Tree in Reigate High Street. I said I'd drive there; I like driving about to unfamiliar places. He'd already asked what kind of wine I liked before we arranged the date. When I arrived, there was a large glass of crisp, white Sauvignon ready for me. A nice man. But after drinking it, I realised I was ridiculously drunk. Far too drunk to drive home. He said I could stay at his; it was a very short walk, and there was plenty of room. I was really embarrassed at not being able to take my drink, and grateful to him. When we arrived at his place, I remember it being immaculate. A modern, designer-type affair, with lots of glass and steel. Then he begged me to sleep with him. He said, "We don't have to have sex, we can just cuddle up." But I wasn't so drunk as to go for that, so he politely ushered me into a spare room, with a bed made up ready (which I thought was odd) with Egyptian cotton bedding and an expensive-looking beige throw and matching scatter cushions. I collapsed onto the bed and woke up at about 2 am in a corridor, having had the most bizarre dream about walking around corridors in a hospital. Then I woke up again and realised that the previous time I'd woken up, I was actually still dreaming. It was the weirdest night I've ever had. The next morning, he pressed me to stay for breakfast, but I made my excuses and left. As I shut his front door behind me, I was so violently sick, I couldn't do a thing about it. All over his immaculate front lawn, and down my velvet jacket.'

'It was a date rape drug, wasn't it?' says Stephen. 'In the Sauvignon?'

'When I told my friends about it, that's what they said.'

'That's why the wine was waiting for you when you arrived', says Stephen. 'I *do* tell the girls, you know, in here, to watch their drinks.'

'You need to tell the boys, too', says Olivia.

'Slipped a date rape drug by a judge!' says Ivy.

'I might put up a sign or something', says Stephen, 'warning people not to leave their drinks unattended'.

'Wouldn't that make customers think this place is a bit dodgy?' says Ivy.

'Oh dear, yes, maybe...'

'Perhaps he wasn't a judge. Perhaps he'd made that up', says Olivia.

'Were you, you know, alright afterwards?' asks Ivy.

'I don't think anything happened that night, other than the strange dreams that weren't dreams. Hallucinations, I suppose. I searched online for judges called Kevin, and couldn't find any', says Olivia.

'I think he could have been a judge', says Stephen. 'Posh, right, from public school?'

'Well, yes.'

'Because public schoolboys don't know how to talk to women. They... we want to desperately, but don't know how. So it doesn't surprise me, sadly.'

'Well that *is* sad', says Olivia.

'It's outrageous', says Ivy. 'Although, I'm glad you can talk to us, now, Stephen.'

'I bet that was the last time you used that app!' says Stephen.

It wasn't, but there was no way Olivia can talk about that in the pub, so she simply smiles and nods.

***

Ivy accepts Olivia's invitation to pop in for a nightcap on her way back up the hill to No. 11.

'That wasn't the last blind date I had', says Olivia, as they settle down on the sofa, each with a Bailey's on ice.

'Would you like to tell me about it?'

'It's a long story', says Olivia, twizzling the ice in her glass with her finger.

'I have time, if you have time.'

'Well, remember the dry cleaner?'

'When it was a choice between the possibly-judge and the other one on the app?'

'Yes. After Kevin, I decided I might be safer with the dry cleaner. With apologies to sexy dry cleaners everywhere, he wasn't how I expected a dry cleaner to be. He was incredibly attractive; an amateur boxer. He was also half way through an Open University English degree. He was from Wigan originally, but now lived in Streatham. Our first date was in London, at a trendy bar he'd chosen, but it was so noisy we couldn't hear each other speak, so we ended up walking around the city, looking at the shimmering Christmas lights, exclaiming, 'Oo!' and 'Wow!' as if we were at a firework display. The shop windows were decorated with lights, baubles, gifts tied with satin ribbons and bows, Christmas trees with gold and silver swags. Wherever you looked, the city was twinkling and glowing. A first date, so I'd said I'd get the train home at ten, and he gallantly walked me to Charing Cross. Then down came the rain, but we didn't feel like hurrying; we just let ourselves enjoy the sound of it bouncing off the roads and pavements, and sauntered along the Strand, him in his long, black coat, me in my red leather jacket, getting soggy, but not caring. Phil stopped next to a street light beaming white into a rain-washed sky. He put his arm around my waist, and pulled me closer. With the lights reflecting on wet pavements, the sounds, and the droplets landing softly on our eyelashes, I couldn't resist. He caught the train home with me.'

'So romantic!'

'Ah, well, I hadn't been with Phil long before I began to realise he was a bit of a tosser.'

'Oh dear!'

'That's unfair. Maybe what I mean is, we weren't suited. He was a typical old-fashioned northern bloke, who thought women should be at home cooking and looking pretty while men went out and did macho things like building and playing football.'

'And dry cleaning, presumably.'

'Yes. I didn't know people like that still existed. It was also starting to dawn on me that he had a nasty little temper, and he said something about a man at work who'd "had to give his wife a slap", as if that was the natural order of things. Anyway, because we'd talked about how we'd have Christmas dinner at my place, and he'd whinged so much about how lonely he'd been the previous Christmas, I resolved to wait until after the festivities to dump him. Then I underestimated the effect of two glasses of mulled wine at the Christmas market – I'm not much of a drinker – and what with that and a glass of Chardonnay with our meal at the pizzeria, I had to leave in a taxi, before we'd even got to the tiramisu. Phil was angry, I could tell by his face. He helped me upstairs. I collapsed into bed, and said, "I'm sorry, but I'm not up to having sex tonight." I don't remember any more about that night. A few weeks later, there I was staring in disbelief at the plastic test kit stubbornly showing two pink lines.'

'No!'

'When I first confronted Phil with the pregnancy test, I asked him why he hadn't at least worn a condom, and he said, "Naughties". That was it, just "naughties", as if he was talking about a dog peeing on the carpet.'

'Oh, gawd.'

'Yes. For a brief moment, I considered a termination. If I kept the baby, I'd be a single parent, and I was quite old to be having a baby. Yet, if I had the child, I'd only be sixty on its sixteenth birthday. That wasn't so bad, was it? I mean, we don't get our pension now until we're sixty-seven. The thing was, in the time it had taken me to work that out, I had decided I already loved my baby and that was that.'

'I can understand that. Totally. What was Phil's attitude, though?'

'I suppose it's fair to say Phil and I were both in shock for a while. He was fifty, and phoned round his large family, proudly telling them the news. They were saying sickening things like, "Life in the old dog yet", and chuckling. His grown-up daughters were appalled. His parenting had been so atrociously bad that – because of his behaviour – both of them had struggled with their mental health growing up. I won't say any more about that, but trust me, you didn't want this man for a father.

'Then one night I got in my car and just drove and drove, and I found myself in a *Travelodge*. I just had to get away from everything. I turned up at about 11pm, the receptionist staring at the floor next to me where my luggage should have been. The next morning, everything seemed clear. I drove straight to his house, told him it was over, grabbed the few bits and pieces I'd left there, and drove away. I haven't seen him since – don't want to.'

'Hasn't he ever tried to contact you?'

'No, he couldn't care less. He's probably just glad not to be paying maintenance.'

'So there you were, single, and in your... what? Forties?'

'Forty-three. The GP convinced me I should have amniocentesis. He referred to it as a "geriatric pregnancy" and warned me I should be wary of abnormalities.'

'Oh, dear, yes, I suppose so. What was it like?'

'Oh, well, It didn't hurt; it was just weird. Well, other-worldly. In the clinic, they gave me a local anaesthetic, and

– as the gynaecologist and I watched on a screen – a long, thin needle was passed through my belly into my womb, to take a sample of amniotic fluid for analysis. As the needle intruded on her private world, my baby turned around, like a little inquisitive alien, to inspect the needle. "Incredible" is an overused word, but seeing my daughter inside my womb really was, and I will never forget it. Of course, I didn't know she was a girl until they phoned me with the result. They give you the option to know your baby's sex, and I was too impatient to wait. And, no; no abnormalities. Don't ask me what I would have done if there *had* been. I honestly don't know.'

'I don't know what I would have done, either', says Ivy, grateful to have never needed to think about it. She thinks of Ian and wonders if his learning disability was the reason his mother rejected him and his brother when she came to visit them in the Barnardo's home.

'Explaining to my friends how I'd become unexpectedly pregnant, I found myself saying things like, "I was made pregnant against my will." It wasn't me that first used the word "rape". Rape wasn't a subject I'd thought about. It conjured images of back alleys, or men with fists, knives; not falling asleep drunk in bed and waking up pregnant.'

'Yes, I know what you mean.'

'But then I thought about what Phil had done. He knew I'd said no. I tried to imagine him having sex with me while I was sedated by the alcohol. It was as if he'd used me as a blow-up doll. Then once that word, "rape", was there, it grew bigger, and bigger, until it was four giant red capital letters that hovered in front of my eyes every moment of every day. I didn't know what to do with my anger. Then

I realised the obvious thing to do with it was to take it to the police.'

'That makes sense.'

'I prepared what I was going to say, so that I wouldn't scream the place down in fury, or dissolve into tears. The police station waiting area was small and scruffy, with leaflets about domestic violence and shoplifting drooping from holders on the walls. The receptionist was an older woman in a smart grey trouser suit. From behind her screen, she listened to me carefully. "I want to report a rape", I heard myself say. "Let's get you a cup of tea", she said. Her kindness set me off crying. She said she'd call WPC Coote – I'll never forget that name – the WPC on duty who was from the specialist team trained to deal with this sort of thing. "Promising", I thought.

'PC Coote had blonde hair in two shiny pigtails, which seemed to jiggle inappropriately as she spoke. She set about interrogating me. "Were you still with this boyfriend at the time, or had you split up?" I explained we were still together, because of the Christmas thing, but that I'd said no – the last thing I remembered was firmly saying no. I wasn't prepared for her next question: "Why didn't you take the morning after pill?" It was such a ridiculous thing to ask...'

'What did that have to do with it?' Araminta was feeling angry on Olivia's behalf. She looked at Liv's sweet face and wondered how WPC Coote can have been that heartless.

'She was implying I'd got pregnant on purpose. Particularly at my age, it was ridiculous! I was so flustered by her seeming to imply it was all my fault, that I was still stuttering and umming when she said, "Why don't you just go home and enjoy your baby?"

'No!'

'What do you say to that? I'd realised by then that the reason I hadn't taken the morning after pill was that it's only effective for a few days after sex, so there would have been no point because I didn't know I was pregnant – or what Phil had done to me – until weeks later when my period was late. But that was the response to the previous question. I was currently stuck on "Why don't you just go home and enjoy your baby?"

'I left the police station almost spitting with fury. I'd gone in angry about being raped, and come out angry about being raped by a man and shafted by a policewoman. I received a letter from a Detective Sergeant a few weeks later. It said... Hang on a minute...' Olivia stands up, goes to the next room, and returns with a letter. 'Look at this!' She puts the letter on Araminta's lap. It has a police force emblem at the top. 'This bit.' Olivia points to the final paragraph:

...you were in an intimate relationship with Mr Ward, to which there was ongoing consent to sexual activity. The activity in which Mr Ward failed to use a condom did not breach the consent that you had been satisfied to yield him during the relationship. The Police have to prove that Mr Ward knew you did not consent or was reckless as to whether you did not consent. We cannot show this in the circumstances you have described to PC Coote.

'That's just awful. The law's changed now, hasn't it?'

'Maybe, but I'm not sure the attitude has. The only thing that helped with my anger was the offer from a friend to send some people from Brixton to teach him a lesson.

Sometimes when Phil's stupid face unexpectedly springs up in my mind like a Jack-in-the-box, I wish I'd said yes.

'I didn't want to be angry when I was pregnant. I was sure it would have an effect on the baby. And I worried as she grew up and learned to speak, and question, how was I going to explain why we weren't with her father?'

'"Father" is too good a word for him!'

'I resolved I would have to try and love her more than a longed-for child. As she grew, I'd be watching her; trying not to search for traces of him; hoping her hair would be fair, not dark, her eyes not blue. As she reached her teens, I'd want her to be wary of men, but if I taught her not to trust, it would be wrong. I had to take all those thoughts to the waste land at the back of my mind, dig a deep pit, and bury them. Hope no one would dig them up. Hope I wasn't planting them. Hope they wouldn't grow.'

'This is so hard for you. I'm so sorry you have to go through it.' Ivy's words sound hollow to her. 'I wish I could think of something better to say.'

'It's OK. You don't have to say anything clever. It's helpful for me; you listening to my story. Anyway, this is how I coped: It occurred to me that, because I would never have chosen to have a baby as a forty-three-year-old single parent, the only way this child could have come into being was if it happened without my choice. So it followed that she was meant to be. I was going to call her Kismet.'

Ivy noticed that the furrows in Olivia's brow that had been there while she was telling her story had disappeared at the mention of her daughter's symbolic name.

'Such a lovely, special name! It means 'destiny', doesn't it?'

'Yes, or 'God's will', if you're religious.'

'That's beautiful. You found meaning in your distress.'
'I think I had to, or I would have remained angry; bitter.'
'Well, thank you, Liv, for trusting me with your story.'
'You have one of those faces.'
'I've been told. Now, just before I go, I need your advice.'
'About?'
'My daughter keeps pressuring me to try the dating app again. What do you think?'
'Oh. Well...' Olivia frowns.
'You think I'm too old?'
'No, not that at all, it's just that you must stay safe. Watch your drink. Meet in a public place and have a safe route out of there to get home, or to leave early if you need to.'
'It sounds like *Mission Impossible!*'
They sing the theme tune to *Mission Impossible* and laugh together, as Ivy stands up to leave.
'Shh... we mustn't wake Fran', giggles Olivia.
'We're friends, aren't we, now?' asks Ivy.
Olivia puts her head on the side and smiles straight onto Ivy's eyes.
'Yes, now you've stopped pretending you're someone else.'
'You heard me, didn't you?' asks Ivy. 'That time I broke my nail putting that invitation through your letterbox, and swore. Loudly.'
'Oh, I wondered what you were swearing at', smiles Olivia. 'Yes, Ivy, we are definitely friends.' She leans forward to give Ivy a tight hug.
Ivy bites her lip, afraid she's about to cry.
'Oh no', says Olivia, 'what's wrong?'
'That's the first time anyone's touched me in years.'

'Oh, Ivy!' says Olivia, and hugs her again.

***

As Ivy leaves Olivia's house, the darkness momentarily engulfs her, but when she reaches the street light outside her own house, she smiles. She thinks of how Olivia coped with her trauma by naming her daughter Kismet. Ivy wishes she'd found meaning in her own experiences, and wonders whether she's still bitter with the world about being born poor, about losing her little brother, Michael, and being ridiculed for her poverty by Mean Jean, the very person she was most jealous of because Jean's family could afford a doctor. Maybe, she thinks, realising all this is starting to melt her icy bitterness. She couldn't help being born poor any more than Jean could help being born wealthy. As Ivy, she doesn't need to pretend to be like wealthy people; that hasn't brought Michael back, nor has it made her life immune to sadness. She looks across at Beatrice's house, and thinks she doesn't need to despise wealthy people, either.

She pauses outside her front door for a moment to take in the view of Secret Street at night. With the white light from the lamp posts, and glow from lights shining in people's windows, it looks like a scene on a Christmas card; full of joys to come, and peaceful. She turns her key in the lock.

21 Secret Street – Aslan

A week before the Platinum Jubilee party

'I'm just so grateful to you.' Ivy has popped down the road to Aslan, to thank him for helping her with the bailiffs.

'I am pleased to help. There was no one there to help our family when we needed it, so I am pleased to be able to help you.'

Ivy brandishes a box of cakes.

'Wahey, mini Battenbergs!' says Aslan. His eyes light up like a child's.

'They're Mr Kipling; not Aldi. Don't tell Beatrice', Ivy laughs.

'You will stay for a while. We will have a cup of tea with them. English tea; Yes?'

'That would be lovely.'

Ivy follows Aslan into his kitchen where he puts the kettle on, and takes two mugs out of the cupboard above the kitchen counter. Ivy stares at the mugs, thinking of Aslan's reaction to dropping a cup in her house at the meeting last week.

'I know what you are thinking. It was embarrassing for me. It is what they call a "trigger" nowadays; a trauma reaction. Do you want to know about it?'

'Well, yes, if you want me to know about it.'

'My counsellor I used to see, he says the more times you tell your story, the less it has power over you. I have not told it many times. It is not an easy story to hear. Some of it is a happy story, but it starts with the bad. What do you think? You want to hear it?'

Looking into his blue eyes, Ivy thinks she can see a little boy inside this great big, shaven-headed, bear of a man. She remembers moments thinking this when listening to Jed and Ben. Maybe she's seeing what therapists call "the inner child".

'Yes. I would be honoured to hear your story, Aslan.'

'The cup, you see; if I dropped a cup at home, if I was clumsy, my father was very angry. I still have dreams of him beating us; my brother and sisters and me.'

Ivy and Aslan are now in his brightly painted yellow living room. They sit down on the comfy sofa, with their tea and cakes on the pine coffee table in front of them.

Aslan takes a deep breath in and out.

'Last night I had the dream again. It is about thirty years ago. I am back in our flat in Turkey. I am nine years old. I sit on the wide, red leather sofa, with my brother and sisters. I have to hold up my sister, Safiya's leg, while our father beats on the soles of her feet with a stick.'

'A stick? I don't understand.'

'A stick about a metre long. It is a stick from a hazel tree, worn smooth with use. This is "falaka"; a well-known punishment in Turkey. Safiya, ten, is crying, and it is my turn next. When my father has finished beating on Safiya's feet, she holds up my leg while father beats on the soles of my feet. I do not cry, because I am learning to be a man. Then I hold up Emira's leg. She is seven. Emira cries; her whole body squirms, but I have to grip onto her leg. She's still crying when she has to hold up Halil's legs. He is five. When father beats on Halil's feet, Halil screams like a girl. Afet, twelve, was beaten first because she is the oldest. Afet tries to stay calm because she wants to look after us; show us it's not so bad and it will soon be over. She bites her lip. Afterwards, we hobble away. We do not talk to each other much. The pain will die away over the next day or so, but we will never forget this; the wide, red sofa, the falaka, the stick, the screams. Sometimes, as I did last night, we will feel the pain again in our dreams.'

Ivy struggles to take this in. Aslan can't be older than his late forties; it can't have been that long ago. How can this be acceptable? She doesn't want to interrupt by asking his age.

'We had falaka regularly. We didn't know why. Maybe it was to make us strong. Father beat us up, too, especially when he had been drinking raki. Sometimes it seemed he was always drinking raki. We had another brother once. His name was Kaplan. Father beat him so bad Kaplan had to go to hospital. They couldn't save him.'

Ivy can't quite believe what she's hearing. The cheerful yellow of Aslan's living room seems incongruous.

'Our father had two wives. It's old-fashioned now, but back then in Turkey it was more common for the man to have two or three wives in the house. He had seven or eight children with his other wife. But the two wives didn't get on. The first wife was hitting my mother because she was jealous, and my father said, "OK, she's not going to take this any more, I'll just take my second wife and be gone." He brought us – my mother, my brother and sisters and me – to live in a block of flats in the city. Father loved our mother very much, but he was a cruel man, and he beat her, too. It was chaos at home; screaming and shouting in our house every day. I was being beaten, but my sisters suffered as well because they were watching it. Most painful was having to watch Mummy get beaten up. Not once, not twice, but on a weekly basis. I'd be about ten and we would be woken up in the night because he was beating her and she was yowling like a trapped cat. Sometimes she would try to hide between us, but we were little children; what could we do apart from watch between our fingers? Sometimes he dragged her along the floor by her beautiful long, brown hair. She had bald patches where he pulled so much of it out.

'But that's not why we left Turkey.'

Aslan takes a few breaths in and out. 'This next part is about sexual abuse. You OK to be hearing it?'

'I will be alright. Thank you for checking.'

'Sometimes at night, father was touching us inappropriately. He came to my room when I was in bed, pushed my pyjamas down, and his hand went down... From when I was about ten until I was thirteen. Me and my sisters and brother, we didn't talk about it, but I asked Afet a few years ago and she said yes; her, too, unfortunately. I wanted to know why; why did these horrible things happen to us? Were we just in the wrong place at the wrong time? Then I realised it's happening to a lot of people, but no one's talking about it. Like I said, I've seen a counsellor and talked about it now; it's good to get these things out.'

Ivy feels ashamed for hating her father because he wanted her to be a boy. He hadn't beaten her, or interfered with her sexually. How petty she had been to hang on to that grudge for so long.

'The real sexual abuse – the worst – wasn't my father. I had cousins, maybe six or seven years older than me. I remember my aunt's son kissing me and touching me like I'm a woman, and then going on top of me and trying to get inside. I remember pain a couple of times. I remember stuff a young boy that age shouldn't experience. A man should have that experience with a woman, maybe when he's eighteen or older; not that young. This went on for a couple of years, then my father found out and he had a big fight with them. Not that him going round to pick a fight with them helped. The shame, it clings to me, even now – sticks to me like a shadow.

'But that's not why we left.

'The other family – the first wife's family – they hated us, even though we were just children, and none of this was our fault. We still saw them; they used to visit us. They wanted Father back. Even though they were getting beaten up by him, they still wanted him around because in Turkey you need the protection of a father. If you've got no parents, anything can happen to you. You can end up on the streets, on drugs, in a whorehouse getting raped for years and years – doesn't matter if you're a boy or girl – Turkey can be a very dangerous place. No social services; no children's homes.'

Ivy's eyes widen.

'Yes, it's true, unfortunately. The police are not as strong as in UK; you have to protect yourself. That's what the father does. It's a man-based culture in Turkey; women are basically second class. It's changing these days, but in my childhood the man had all the power in Turkey. Women were allowed to divorce their husbands, though. It wasn't easy, but it could be done. In the end, Mummy divorced our father. I'm about fourteen now. I remember the day he leaves. Even though he's a cruel man, we still love him. We're all standing on the stairs watching him go out of the front door with his bags and Mummy's saying, "That's it; you're not going to see your father any more", and we're all crying.

'Now that he's gone, it's quiet in our flat. But we're still not safe, because we have no father to protect us. Men would come and try to have sex with my beautiful sisters, and with Mummy, too. Sometimes older men, trying it on. And it's not a nice neighbourhood; there's often people fighting. One day we're on the balcony and we see a man fall from the fifth floor of the block opposite. He crashes on the ground, and we see him lying there on the grey paving stones, a lake of blood growing wider and wider around his smashed-up head. He dies on the way to hospital. We're children. We don't want to be seeing things like that; we want to be seeing ice cream, we want to be seeing our mummy smiling, saying loving things to us, not a man dropping from a balcony, his head exploding...'

Ivy nods.

'But that's not why we left.

'Back then there was a war in Turkey; there were Kurdish groups fighting against the Turkish army. The Kurds were suffering. They even gave them a different ID card to show they're Kurdish. Those days it was bad; you weren't even allowed to speak the Kurdish language in Turkey. Kurdish people would be arrested, beaten up, or sometimes they are "disappeared". These days it's getting better and better; Kurdish language is permitted; there are Kurdish TV channels. But back then it was bad.'

'So you're Kurdish?'

'Mummy is Kurdish. We had to keep it quiet. That's why Afet, Safiya, Emira, Halil and me, we all have Turkish names. She was lonely, too. She did not dare to try and make friends among the local Turkish women. When we were out in public with her, we had to be careful not to call her by the Kurdish word, "Mummy" (it's the same as English), but "Ana", the Turkish word. Sometimes the little ones, Emira or Halil, if they were out with Mummy at the market, they'd forget, and say that dangerous word, and she had to shush them, leave her shopping and hurry away. We always hoped no one was listening, and especially not the secret police: MIT. That's short for Milli İstihbarat Teşkilatı; the National Intelligence Organisation. They're not walking around in uniform, but they're still police officers; a special team, with casual clothes, but a gun in their belt.'

'Like our MI5?'

'Maybe, yes. Nobody knows what they're checking out, but they're a formidable team working for the Turkish government. You couldn't deal with these guys. If they wanted, they could easily kill you; get rid of the whole of your family.

'When I had to do my National Service, I was young, clean-shaven, handsome.' Aslan grins and flutters his eyelashes.

Ivy remembers hearing Ben's story, and Jed's, and how they both had a habit of laughing when they mentioned trauma and sadness. 'No wonder there are so many middle-aged men killing themselves', she thinks. 'They need to start to cry – not laugh – when they're thinking of unbearable things that have happened to them'.

'So, yes, they chose me to be close protection for the general's wife. Wherever she went, I followed. I had to have special training in shooting and close fighting because it can be dangerous for Turkish army families. It was horrible; carrying a gun, licensed to kill. I didn't want to kill anybody and I didn't want to be killed. And it's while I'm in the army I see first-hand how they treat the Kurds. I'm doing army duty in a Kurdish city, watching outside the general's house. I see a man – a young Kurdish man – just walking by, not doing anything, and the Turkish soldiers they take him and put him in their car, and they beat him up. I'm watching it through the car window; their fists, his head, and bleeding... he's helpless.

'But that's not why we left.

'My second-oldest sister, Safiya, she married an American soldier, and he gets stationed all over Europe. They're in Italy for a while, and then in the UK. And our sister said to us – because she knew we were struggling in Turkey – that everything is much better there; we could be safe there. In the UK it doesn't matter if you don't have a father or older brothers to protect you, and it's fine if you're Kurdish; no one's going to come and kill you, or beat you up. So then we start thinking about coming to the UK. It would take a lot of planning, and money we didn't have, but it might be worth it if we could be safe there.

'But still, we didn't leave yet.

'By then, my older sister, Afet; she is nineteen. She is beautiful, with long, wavy hair the colour of chestnuts, and big brown eyes. She's lively, and funny; always making people laugh. I think maybe she developed that sense of humour because she was always trying to cheer us up when times were hard. Men were attracted to Afet. She started going out with an older man; Emir. He was a bit flashy, you know? In his designer clothes, with his big black Mercedes. He had his hair style in a sort of... What do you call it?' Aslan makes a sweeping gesture across the top of his head.

'A quiff?'

'Yes, maybe a quiff. He had this way of sweeping his fringe back as if he was in a shampoo advert. I think Afet thought that if Emir became part of our family, he would protect us. After a couple of dates, he tells Afet he's in MIT. And when he says that, Afet remembers that morning when he came to call on her, my younger brother, Halil, had called out to our mother, "Mummy". Afet comes home shaking. She tells us Emir knows that Mummy is Kurdish. He will lose all respect for Afet. He could even tell the Turkish authorities and they could come and drag Mummy out of the house and take her away. But Emir had already arranged the next date with Afet. What should she do?'

'She was damned if she went, and damned if she didn't', says Araminta.

'Yes', says Aslan, 'and what could I do? I'm the oldest boy in the family – the man of the house – I'm supposed to protect her. Halil – always the reckless one – he says, "Let me take on Emir; I'll finish him off!" He's quivering with anger. I have to calm him down, even though in my heart I want to do the same'.

'What on earth did you do?'

'There was nothing we could do. Afet decided she had to go on the date. That evening, she put on a fake smile along with her makeup, you know?'

Ivy nods.

'Emir picked her up at the door. Halil and I hid around the corner, ready to follow, staying back, waiting until we thought he couldn't see us in his mirrors, then running behind his car as fast as we could. But he revved up around the next corner, and zoomed off out of sight. All we could do was go home and wait.

'Afet was home sooner than we expected. She struggled to get her key in the door, so I went to open it for her. She was standing there with a look of terror on her face. I put my arm around her and brought her inside, sat her down. She started to cry. She tells us that Emir had tried to rape her. It happened in his car, and she managed to get out and run away. She thought he'd jump out and chase after her, but he didn't. Now what can we do? Is he going to come back and finish the job? We can't protect her. If we fight that man, we will all be killed. If it goes to court, they will just close the case and he'll go free because he works for the government. That was the moment we thought, "That's it, there's no life here for us in Turkey any more." That's why we left.'

'So you all left together?'

'No, we all came separately. Afet has to leave quickly. She has a friend who lives in a town about fifty kilometres away. She packs that night, and goes off on the train to stay with her. From there she will obtain a student visa, and go to England to study at a language college. Safiya is already married, and living at an army base with her husband in Germany, so Mummy leaves on the train, and goes there to stay with them.

'That evening, Emir came round to ask where Afet was; she hadn't been answering his calls. I wanted so badly to punch him, but I had to remain calm; I could see the gun on his belt. I said Afet had gone to stay with an auntie who was ill, to help look after her children. I said it was an emergency and she hadn't had time to let anyone know. He just sneered, swept his fringe back, and left. I assumed he accepted the story, but it wouldn't be long before he realised Afet was gone for good. One evening two weeks later, Halil sees Emir's Mercedes drive up and park in the road outside our block of flats. Emir rings the door bell, and we don't answer; just sit there, quivering like cowards.

'Emira, she's engaged by now. Her fiancé gets fake passports for them, and they travel to the UK, no problem, and declare themselves asylum seekers when they arrive. It's completely legal to be an asylum seeker as long as you declare yourself to the authorities when you arrive. Did you know this?'

'I didn't, I'm afraid.'

'It's a big problem for us; people think we are illegal when we are not.' He shakes his head.

'I apologise for my ignorance', says Ivy.

Aslan smiles.

'You are not an ignorant person. I think not so many people know this law; you know? He sighs. Anyway, now it was only Halil and me left in Turkey. There had already been two occasions when the doorbell had gone, and we hadn't answered. Who else could it be, but Emir? I'm working as a builder's mate, so I have a little money. Halil's still at school, so he has no income at all, and I pay for Halil's train fares. He travels the three-thousand-mile journey to the ferry terminal at Calais, jumps in the back of a big Volvo estate and hides in the luggage. Then, when the car's safely on the ferry, he gets out, and walks up to the passenger deck with all the others. When he arrives at the customs at Dover, they ask for his passport, and he says, "Here's my ID; I have no passport, but I want to claim asylum." No trouble at all! Can you imagine that?'

'I can't', says Ivy, smiling.

'And then one day on the way home from work, I see Emir's Mercedes driving towards me. I was pretty distinctive back then, with a shaved head and earrings, so I pull the hood of my sweatshirt up over my head and run into the nearest alley. Had he seen me? Money or no money, I had to get on with it and leave. There's no way I would do what my little brother did; it was such a huge risk. I only knew what he'd done when I heard his voice tell me on a phone call from England that he had arrived safely at Afet's flat in London. I want to be angry with him – putting himself in so much danger like that – but he is so happy that I just have to be happy for him. His journey was stupidly easy. But for me, things always seem to be complicated.

'The best place to look for a people-smuggling organisation is in the Kurdish communities.'

'Because they're at risk, so they use the people smugglers a lot?'

'Yes. I just need to go in the coffee shops and start asking around, then the next thing I know, a little piece of paper is slipped into my jacket pocket. I leave the coffee shop, and walk round the corner into an alley where I'm alone. I unfold the piece of paper and see it has a phone number on it. I ring it. It's a man speaking English, but he has a Romanian accent. With my English I learned in lycée, I understand that he's saying it costs £2,500 per person. I phone Afet. She's already making good money by now, working in a casino in London. It's fun, and what she loves most is that there, being beautiful is not a risk. Afet hasn't worked there long enough yet to have any money saved up, but she has an interesting new friend – one of the regulars at the casino – a wealthy elderly Chinese man called Jin. He tells her his name means 'gold', and laughs. Maybe he sees himself as a father figure, or maybe he just likes being seen with a beautiful young woman. Either way, he's kind to Afet, and when he hears about my predicament, he doesn't even think twice; he says he'll pay.'

'Wow! So how exactly do you pay the people smugglers?'

'The money is to be paid to a middle man, once I've arrived in England. Afet won't tell me more than that. The fewer people that know his name, the better. The risk feels enormous, but I ring the şebeke – the organisation – and tell them yes. I am now in their hands.'

'I get myself a tourist visa, and pack as much as I can take with me in one big rucksack.'

'It must have been so hard; leaving your home.'

Ivy thinks of her childhood home, and wonders if there were things about Taunton she missed.

'Was there anything that you were particularly sad to leave behind?'

'I hated having to leave my PlayStation and Formula 1 game; there's no way I could fit them in my bag.'

Ivy pictures Aslan as a boy; barely a man, playing his computer games, and realises how young he was when he had to deal with all this.

'I travel by train to Italy, and from there on to Germany to join Safiya and Mummy. I am on trains for days, leaving my home forever; watching my country framed in the train carriage window, as if it is a series of paintings, you know? The next time I'm on a train, I won't be in a seat, I'll be stacked like a box in a freight wagon.

'From Germany, Safiya and Mummy drive me to Paris in their Ford estate; some place the şebeke had told us to meet them, on the outskirts of the city where there are so many blocks of flats, it's hard to see the sky. It reminds me a bit of the neighbourhood where I grew up. I'm half expecting some poor man to suddenly fall from a balcony to his death below. The şebeke told me to bring nothing – no phone, no luggage – only ID. I have to wait there to be picked up. Mummy and Safiya keep driving round the block to see if I am still there; if I'm safe. Then a car stops, a man asks, "Are you Aslan?" I nod and get in the car, and I'm gone.

'The man who picks me up is Turkish. He says, "Don't worry, I'm going to take you to England." He takes me to this apartment block, somewhere in Paris. I don't know where because the organisation doesn't want me to know. We walk up a spiral staircase, past lots of doors, up to the top floor, then there's a scuffed white door, and we go through it into a little flat with a small room. It's maybe four metres square, with just one small skylight window. There are two sofas, and then just carpets on the floor. They lock me in. I'm thinking, "If something happens, how will I run away if I'm locked in? What if there's a fire?"'

'Oh, lawks, yes!'

'The first day I'm on my own. The second day, a couple more people come, then the next day, a few more. In the end there are about fourteen or fifteen of us, including a woman and her two little children. They're mainly Turkish-Kurdish. We're locked in that flat for four days. They have to lock us in; we're an investment. Fifteen people at £2,500 each; you can tell how much money they're making.'

'Did they bring you food?'

'They bring bottles of water, and sandwiches made from baguettes, with cheese, or spread with butter and strawberry jam. There were biscuits in little wrappers with *BN* on them; sometimes red ones with jam, sometimes brown with chocolate. Most people sleep on the floor. I sleep on the sofa, and nobody bothers me, so I ask, "Why nobody's come to share the sofa with me?" and they say, "You relax." They're treating me as if I'm part of the şebeke, but I say, "I'm just like you – I'm trying to go, just like you're trying to go!" So I push them to come join me on the sofa to sleep. You couldn't really call it sleep, though.

'On the fourth day, they come. They have a white van and a white BMW. They like me straight away. Maybe I was a little more educated than the other Turkish-Kurdish there, I don't know, but they put everybody in the van, including the woman and two kids, and they ask me to ride in the BMW with them. They take us to this deserted industrial place. There are old empty warehouses; the sort of buildings the bad guys in a film take some poor victim to be tied to a chair and tortured. One of the buildings has lights on. They beckon to us to get out of the vehicles and go inside. Then it feels like playing – what do you call it when children play and one hides and the others look?'

'Hide-and-seek?'

'Yes, hide-and-seek. The şebeke people run out of the building to a corner across the yard, and they say, "OK, two of you run to us." So we run, two or three at a time, through the shadows, until we're all out of the building and crouching in a clump of bushes, next to a row of about ten railway tracks. It took at least ten minutes to get us all there. Then, at midnight, we follow the şebeke along the tracks in the dark, next to the trains. And I remember –

as if it had just happened – along comes a passenger train, and inside are all these people, smiling, joking. They're so happy and free! Normal people, safe people, with passports and freedom and no MIT to worry about; no psychopathic fathers, or rapists to worry about; no war to worry about. And they're going where we're going. I just remembered that; it was wonderful.'

Ivy tries to picture it. A train carriage full of "normal", happy people, and being on the outside, looking in.

'But we won't be riding in a comfortable carriage; we're going to jump on a waggon in a freight train, and travel like goods to be bought and sold; like heaps of coal, or lengths of timber. The organisation walk us to the waiting place; a clump of horse chestnut trees and overgrown, straggly buddleia bushes. This is going to be our home for the next four days. We're just told to wait there; be patient. Only the şebeke know which train we have to get on.

'Our new home consists of a mud floor, with nettles and cow parsley between the trees and bushes. We had to designate an area for our toilet, and the only thing I can say about this whole thing that makes me laugh is that I'll never forget stinging my backside on nettles. Having no toilet paper, and trying to use leaves to wipe ourselves was less funny.'

'Uggh! We had to use newspaper for toilet paper when we were young', says Ivy, with a grimace.

Aslan laughs; a hearty booming laugh.

'You must have got black print on your backsides.'

Ivy smiles. 'We must have. Anyway, never mind toilet paper, what was it like in those bushes for four days?'

'It was summer, and the sun made its way down through the leaves to warm us. I remember, it was sometimes as if there were splashes of gold on the ground. In the evening, there were big old wood pigeons startling us with the amount of noise they made landing in the trees. We scraped the twigs away from the mud to lie down at night, rolled up our jackets or sweatshirts for pillows, and looked up through the horse chestnut trees at the sky. The sound of the trains was our lullaby. If anyone slept, they were awoken just before sunrise by the dawn chorus. The woodpigeons, going "woo-woo", the blackbirds singing, the blue tits – I remember that, now. Every morning we hope this will be the day that we leave.

'The şebeke bring baguettes and biscuits and bottled water again. By the third day, we notice a family of tame dormice are visiting us, to feast on the crumbs.'

'Aww...'

'Yes. I remember that', Aslan smiles.

'Each time they bring food, the şebeke say to us, "Don't worry; be patient; you're gonna get there in the end." Once they bring a phone and it's the husband of the woman and children. He talks to his wife and she's crying, and then she hands the phone to me. Her husband says, "Please, brother, look after them." How can I say no? From that moment on I feel responsible for them.

'Then we had the first attempt. The şebeke say, "Here! The goods train! Run!" and we start to run, as best we can, jumping over the tracks, placing our feet between all the rails, until we reach the wagons. The şebeke are calling, "This one! Jump! Jump!" But the train isn't on the first of the wide row of tracks; it's way past the middle, and it takes so long to get to the truck, that we're too late, and only the first four of us can get on. The rest of us feel a bit down. We don't know what's going to happen to us.'

Ivy's reminded of Toby's story of rescuing the runaway teenager from the railway tracks at Ashford, and wonders if there's something special about railway lines; about journeys.

'The second attempt was the same. This time about five or six of us get on. It's just me, four other men, and the woman and children left now. The third attempt, they put us on a train, but there's a French man cleaning the trucks, and he sees us jump on; he looks right into my eyes. I try to tell the Romanians, in the best English I can manage, that the man has seen us and it isn't safe, but they don't seem to understand. I wave my hands to try and mime a cleaner and him seeing us, like a game of... what do you call it?'

'Charades?'

'Yes, I think it is this; charades, but the Romanian just says, "It's all OK." We're only on the train a few minutes before we hear footsteps. The French police are marching towards us. They open the door, and say, "Come out! We saw you!" Again, we have failed. And we're scared.'

'Oh no! Did they arrest you, or...?'

'We're taken to a police station in Paris. We have to spend the night there. They put camp beds and blankets in a sports hall; an indoor basketball court. There are a lot of people there like us. They give us food, tell us to be calm and that they'll do the paperwork in the morning. There are police sitting in chairs watching us. Again, we didn't sleep much. The next morning we go across to the police station where they process our paperwork. They say we are free, but we have seven days to leave, and if we're still in France after that, we'll be here illegally.

'We're lucky, there's an interpreter lady there. Not part of the şebeke, but a Turkish interpreter, and she wants to help us. She knows everything about Paris; knows her way around. She says she is going to take the woman and her two children back to her house in the city, but that there is no room for the other five of us. We beg her to take us, too. I say, "I've got no phone, and I don't know who to call, anyway. How do I find this organisation again? I've got nothing; no clothes, ten dollars in my pocket. I don't know my way around Paris. Please, take me, too!" Here I am begging. I'm a man; I shouldn't be begging, that's disgusting! But I feel so scared in that city where I don't know the language. I say maybe she can take me to a Turkish coffee shop and I might be able to stay there.

'We all beg her, keep on and on, and in the end she gives in and takes all of us to her house. We have a shower – that was the best shower ever, after being in the bushes for four days and the basketball court for another. And, I remember, she has a nice sofa and everything, and she gives me some clean socks. I have never enjoyed a pair of socks so much! I don't know why I remember that, but having those socks was beautiful.' Aslan smiles, thinking of the socks, and reaches out to pick up another Battenberg cake from the plate. 'These are good, thank you', he says. 'Anyway, so the woman with the children phones her husband, and he has the number for the şebeke. They say, "Put Aslan on the line", as if I am in charge. The şebeke says to go to the station, and they will come and get us. That lovely family – the interpreter's family – they take us to the station. When we arrive, some of us are scared, trying to hide, but I tell them we still have six days before we are there illegally; there is nothing to worry about.

'So the şebeke come and collect us. Same white van and BMW. They ask me if I think the police will be waiting for us there in the bushes, and I say I didn't think so, not so soon after they arrested us the day before. So they take us again. Same place, same thing, same bushes.'

'Déjà vue.'

'What is that?'

'It's when you suddenly feel as if you've been in that exact same situation before. It's French, it literally means 'seen before'.'

'Yes, we had your déjà vue, then. Some people, they start to panic. They want their money back, but I tell them it's OK; to be calm, "Come on, let's get it done." The organisation, they love me because I don't give them trouble.

'The next day, they put us on a train, no problem.'

Hearing this, Ivy feels her shoulders relax.

'We just jump in', Aslan continues. 'I have that woman and children with me. I promised the husband, so I pushed them up in the truck in front of me. This goods train has carriages with solid sides, and little things with bars at the top; sort of windows.'

'Grilles?'

'Maybe, yes. There are cardboard boxes stacked about half way up the walls. There are glass bottles inside them; whisky. That made me think of my father; the beatings, the chaos and shouting of my childhood. And here I was riding on top of bottles of alcohol! It seemed a good sign. There isn't room to stand fully, so we sit on top of the boxes. The organisation told us it would take about twenty, twenty-five hours to get to England. They said – twice – that we must not make a sound when the train stops. When it's moving, we can laugh, sing, dance, whatever we want, but when the train is still, railway staff in the other carriages, or people outside, might hear us. Here we are with two little children; I think one of them is three, the other four years old. You can imagine what it's like keeping two little children quiet. The mother is good with controlling them, though. She sits next to me with them. I remember saying to them, "When the train stops, you're gonna be quiet, yes? You're not gonna even breathe!"

'For me the worst bit; the really horrible bit, is the dark. As we're travelling, and the day's over, we can see, through the little grilles, the lights outside going out one by one. The thing is, I've always been afraid of the dark. I'm a big, strong man, but I'm still afraid of the dark. So as those lights go out, I have these weird feelings inside me. Then we come to a place where it is so dark that I can't see my hand in front of my face. I feel completely alone, as if I'm in a grave. If I had my phone I could switch the torch on, I would have been alright, but I have nothing; just my papers, like they told us. Maybe we're in a tunnel; I have no idea. But I'm smothered in darkness. I panic; I think I'm going to lose my mind. So I put my hand down, lie down, close my eyes, and I say to God, "I am in your hands." I just lie there and trust in God and wait for the light. I don't want to open my eyes because what's the point if you can't see anything?'

Ivy nods.

'After about an hour I start to sense through my closed eyelids that there is some light. Then I open my eyes. It's morning, and the children are singing "Ali babanın bir çiftliği var...", loudly. It's from a kids' cartoon movie; a sort of Turkish version of Old Macdonald had a Farm. They're enjoying making the animal noises; the sheep going, "Mee! Mee!" the dogs, "Hav! Hav!" It's doing my head in, I can tell you, but they are happy, so I don't stop them. The organisation told us the journey would be about twenty to twenty-five hours, but only fifteen have passed when the train stops. We try and shush the children, but they're having so much fun, they both sing louder, egging each other on. "Mee! Mee!" they're shouting. Their mother is shushing them, saying their names in a loud whisper. I want to put my hands over their mouths, but that's not something you should do to children. I tell them to be quiet, in as stern a voice as you can when you're trying to keep your voice down. Eventually they stop. We listen. At first there's silence, then we hear a sound: boots on gravel. And they're coming closer.'

'Oh, no, not again? You get caught again?'

'Everyone in the railway truck is panicking. The sound of boots marching towards us seems to have gone on for a lifetime, although it can't have even lasted as long as thirty seconds. The children sense something is wrong, and start to cry. It's too late to tell them to be quiet now. I try to be strong. I say to everyone, "Unfortunately we couldn't make it this time. They tell us at least twenty hours and it's only fifteen, so we haven't succeeded." We all feel horrible; hopeless. The thought of being sent back to Paris again is unbearable. We just can't go back there again; we *can't*. Then the door opens and we blink into the daylight. There are three men with dark caps and white shirts.

'These aren't French uniforms – the hats aren't those straight-sided peaked ones that the gendarmes wear – they're English policemen's helmets. They have big blue rectangular badges sewn on their high vis vests with writing that says... I can't believe it... it says, *BRITISH TRANSPORT*

POLICE! There isn't room to jump up and down on top of the crates of whisky, but in my heart I'm jumping up and down. I say to the others, "It's OK, we've done it; we're here! These are British Police." The police call to us, "Come on out, we know you're there." I'll never forget that moment. We made it!

'The transport police drive us to the police station in Dover. They let me call my brother, Halil. My family have been worried over the last five days, hearing nothing from me. To make matters worse, there was another man who'd come to Dover called Aslan three days before, so when my sister had phoned and asked if a Aslan had arrived and they tell her yes, she'd driven all the way from London to Dover only to find it wasn't me. So Afet, Emira and Halil were stressed, and my mum and Safiya in Germany were stressed. They are so happy to get my call! Then Afet speaks to the customs people on the phone and she tells them, "Don't send Aslan anywhere, I come to pick him up." When Afet and Halil arrive in a minicab, even though I am exhausted, I run towards them, and we just hug and smile, and hug some more.

'That night, I have a hot shower at Afet's flat. Halil gives me some clothes; a nice suit and everything. Jin arrives. He's going to help us celebrate, and it's good to be able to thank him for paying the şebeke. First we go for a lovely meal, then – I'm not gonna lie – we go out to a strip club; to Stringfellows. It's crazy; yesterday I was in a railway truck, today I'm dressed in a suit, with my brother and a Chinese man in Stringfellows. Oh my goodness, it is beautiful! I am a young man; only twenty-four. That is the best moment of my life, I love it!' Aslan chuckles.

Ivy feels happy for him; strip club or no strip club.

'So the next day we go to the Turkish solicitors. They have a big office in Wood Green. They look at my case and help me apply for asylum and get my permission to work. We have to follow the legal process and go to court. I get a job working on building sites around London. I'm a big strong guy – "hunky", my wife calls me – so even though it is hard physical work, at first I don't mind it. No one is abusing me. No one is going to shoot me.

'When I'm first here in England I can't understand much more than yes or no; it's frustrating. I'm a grown man, but I don't know how to get the bus, or take the train, or where to go, and my brother and sister have to escort me everywhere, as if I am a baby. So in the evenings I go to an English language school and study the basics, then on to a college to do ESOL.'

'English as a Second Language?'

'Yes. The only thing wrong in my life is the other men at work. They would make silly jokes – sexual things – that upset me. They don't know that every time they do it, my mind goes straight back to my childhood; mine and my brother's and sisters' abuse, my sister's rape attempt. It's horrible. So I decide I want to go and work somewhere different; somewhere that doesn't have this culture. I want a profession. I don't have A Levels, but I find out from the college where I do evening classes that I can do maths there in the evenings after work. Maths was always my best subject at lycée. I pass easily, and I am ready to go to university to study.

'Then the letter arrives...' A dark cloud seems to pass over Aslan's face.

'Don't talk to me about letters', Ivy says.

'Oh, I am sorry, you...'

'No, I was sort of joking, you know, after the bailiffs?'

'Ah, yes, I see. This letter, it says they are taking away my work permits, my health benefits, and I can't work; can't even sign on to get the dole. They don't send me back to Turkey, but I can't work. I haven't done anything wrong. I have to rely on my family for food, money; everything. I go to court, tell them about my mother being Kurdish; about the secret police attacking my sister, but they don't believe me. What am I supposed to do? Rob a bank? Join a gang? I didn't come here to be lazy; I want a chance to work. You know, do something good for myself and the people around me. For two years I have to stay either with my brother or my sister, sleep on their sofa, eat their food. It causes a lot of family arguments. Every two weeks I have to go and sign at the police station. There's no shelter, and if it rains, we get wet, like dogs. I am helpless, like when I was in that railway truck in the dark. After two years of it, and a particularly stressful family argument, I am desperate, so I pray to God, "Please open a door for me."

'The next day the solicitor phones me up. He says, "Aslan, congratulations, you've got Indefinite Leave to Remain!" I am so happy! My whole family is so happy! This time, though, I don't go to Stringfellows; I go and apply for university. You know the rest, I think. I'm an accountant in a nice office in a road off Mount Pleasant. I know that people with my sort of background – the abuse, the bad childhood, all these traumas – it's easy to get lost and end up on drugs, or going and committing crimes. That time in London when I had no work, no permits, it was hard. I got very down, and kept thinking of all the bad things that happened to me. The beatings, the falaka – I think in some ways, they made me stronger, but the sexual abuse, that flooded my whole being with shame. I know now that the shame isn't mine, and I have to tell myself it was the people that did that to me that were the ones who should feel the shame. I saw a psychiatrist and he put me on Prozac. But I'm much better now; strong. I have to keep taking it, but that's the thing with antidepressants: if they work you must keep taking them. And I think where I've come from, what I left behind, and where I am now – it's incredible, yes?'

'Yes, truly incredible!' Ivy feels a fool for "getting lost" as Aslan puts it, after the sadness of her childhood. What she went through was so trivial compared to what Aslan suffered, and still suffers sometimes: being bullied for being different, just as she was bullied for being poor.

'Everyone's doing so well; Mum can't believe it! We've all got our Indefinite Leave to Remain; we've all got good jobs. Afet is a psychologist now, with a PhD; Emira is an accountant, too, and Halil, he has his own plumbing company. We can get on with our lives. If something goes wrong, there's social services, there's the police. Nobody's coming to beat us up; nobody's coming to rape us.

'I wanted to get into the English culture. I like the English; they're nice people. So I was praying to God to send me an English wife. God sent me Lara. She's so beautiful! She just swam up to me in the outdoor swimming pool – the one in Tonbridge – and asked would I like to buy her a coffee afterwards. Sometimes I call her 'Alara'; it's the name of a water fairy in a Turkish fable. In the story, Alara takes all the bad things away from people's hearts, like hate and anger, and makes them capable of true love. Lara understands me. I can be jumpy, after all that trauma, you know? When I get upset at some silly little thing, like I drop something and break it – like your cup at the meeting – she says, "It's OK, everything's alright now, you're safe."

'I believe in Jesus now, after all that's happened. I think He put me on that train in Paris that night, and He brought me here and gave me my job and my beautiful wife. Lara and me, we go to church on Sunday morning and we give thanks to God. Maybe we all come to a point in our life where we have to believe in something; something that's going to change our perspective.'

'Well, that's got me thinking now. I'm not religious, but I believe in something I can't put my finger on; something to do with the connectedness between people. Love, maybe. The Bible says God is love, doesn't it?'

'Perhaps it doesn't matter what it is that we believe in; it might be different for you, but for me it's Jesus.'

'So what do you think, now; looking back on your old life in Turkey?'

'There was a time I couldn't look back because there was nothing good to remember. Now, when I look back at all those traumas, those bad memories make me feel happier because I've passed that. Even though sometimes I still physically feel the pain, it's passed. My life is good now; I managed to survive. And my father, when he used to beat us up, I hated him, I wanted to kill him, but now I swear to God I just say to myself that if my father didn't treat us like that, I wouldn't be as strong today.

'In Turkey they accept that life's full of trauma. Mummy's always showing people a photo of me as a little boy, with my big blue eyes. I look at that face and I imagine it being beaten up by my father, and I think, "How can you even think about hurting such a beautiful thing?" In England,

kids grow up in a much better way. Life's different here –
delicate. That's how it's supposed to be.'

The Platinum Jubilee Street Party

Not a long, smooth, white-tableclothed rectangle, but a glorious higgledy-piggledy clutter of square, rectangular, oval, and circular garden tables in wood, iron, plastic, or wicker. Some with tablecloths made of paper or linen. All with some kind of decoration: fake red, white and blue roses; Union Jack or crown-decorated balloons; jubilee-themed cardboard centrepieces of corgis and crowns. A life-size cardboard cutout of the Queen wearing a powder blue dress and hat, and waving, which Nancy found at the back of the cellar beneath her patisserie. Little children with corgi soft toys, or small, plastic Union Jacks, which are also found stuck in Plasticine as table centrepieces. Large jubilee banners strung across garden gates and fences. Hung across the street from upstairs bedroom windows; a mishmash of bunting made of string and cardboard with potato-printed purple crowns, or hand-sewn cotton in Union Jack, or alternating plain red, white, and blue fabric.

Aoife's teenagers have added red and blue streaks to their Goth hairdos. Everyone's found something jubilee-themed to wear: Beatrice, a pair of tailored blue jeans with a white blouse and red cashmere crew neck; Ivy, who is mingling and introducing herself as 'Ivy; not Araminta any more', in a white blouse beneath a cobalt blue trouser suit with a red carnation buttonhole. Toby – here on sufferance – wears his usual jeans and black sweater, but Hilary has decorated his wheelchair with red, white, and blue balloons. Aoife has a floral dress, and Stephen and Aslan wear Union Jack t-shirts. All the lads from the recovery centre are here, and as per the *Suggestions* list on the party-planners' letters, no one has brought alcohol. Some have mugs of tea, others Coke, or squash, lemonade, or sparkling elderflower cordial.

Food ranges from burgers with little Union Jack flags on cocktail sticks waving from the buns (Aslan and Ben), to cheese and ham, coronation chicken, and cucumber sandwiches, crusts cut off and cut into fingers (Nancy, Aoife, and Beatrice). Dotted around the tables are sausage rolls, as well as a few retro cheese and pineapple sticks, stuck into foil-covered grapefruits. There are cake stands, China plates from kitchen cupboards, and paper plates, displaying Mr Kipling cakes, fresh buns and doughnuts, homemade Victoria sponge, chocolate, and lemon cakes, and Nancy's famous strawberry cupcakes given a Platinum Jubilee upgrade with purple buttercream icing and gold-coloured sugar crowns.

The residents of Secret Street linger way beyond lunchtime, chatting and finding things in common. Ben, Jed, Stephen and Aslan decide to set up a five-a-side football team with Ivy's neighbour, Arthur, who's been nagging them about it in the pub for months. Ivy, Nancy, Olivia, and Aoife resolve to join a yoga class together. Wilf manages to slip out to scrounge by sitting expectantly at each table in turn with the soppiest grin he can muster, and has been slipped two cheese cubes and a sausage roll before being told off by Aoife and sent back indoors.

Councillor Petty's turned up, with red, white, and blue paper flowers around his Panama hat. Ivy considers pointing out he's not a resident of Secret Street, but it feels too much like bullying, so instead she welcomes him politely. He decides he should make a speech. Ivy braces herself for him to take all the credit for the party, but he doesn't. He announces what a joyous occasion this is to come together after the Covid lockdowns. It is. He says the Queen is our constant in an ever-changing world. She is. He proposes a toast to Secret Street, which goes down so well that some people who'd been strangers the day before are moved to hug each other. Ivy accepts a hug from Aoife, who says, 'You done good, girl; you've given us your true, authentic self in friendship'.

'Thanks, Aoife', says Ivy. 'Talking of authenticity, I was thinking I might even stop dyeing my hair and let the grey come through.'

'Oh, I wouldn't go that far!' says Aoife, with a fake grimace.

Ivy giggles. 'I prefer being Ivy. I'll organise the deed poll when this is all sorted.' She points to the *For Sale* sign in her front garden.

'Oh, Ivy, we don't want you to leave, though', says Nancy.

'Gawd, my memory's rubbish, I thought I'd told you; I'm going to buy the garden flat down the hill. The couple at 96A are having a baby, so they'll need somewhere bigger. I'll be debt-free, no mortgage, Aslan repaid, and I'll be next door to Toby and Hils, and just down from Ian.'

Ian's behind Aoife, munching a sandwich.

'Ian will look after the garden for me, won't you, Ian?'

'Yes', he agrees.

'I'll pay the going rate, won't I? We've talked about it, haven't we, Ian?'

'Yes.'

The children are playing a jubilee-themed bingo treasure hunt game that Aoife has devised for them. Kismet rushes past, waving her bingo card.

'I just have to get the pink corgi, and I've won', she shouts, breathlessly.

'Try in the boot', says Aoife.

Kismet runs off to look in the row of wellies outside Aoife's house.

'It's in the car boot; I've left it open', whispers Aoife to the others.

Toby wheels over, stops and puts his brakes on next to Nancy's life-size Queen cutout. Denise, Ben, and Jed come over with him, glasses of fizzing Coke, and plates of jubilee cupcakes in their hands. Ben's been carrying Toby's, and hands them to him.

'It's a lovely party, Ara... sorry, Ivy. It's a lovely party, Ivy', says Denise.

'An excellent Platty Jube!' says Olivia.

'A what?' asks Ivy,

'Platty Jube!'

'Oh, that's 'orrible!' says Ivy. 'It sounds so common.'

'But it's OK to sound common, isn't it?' says Olivia, and gives Araminta a knowing wink.

'Anyway', says Aoife, 'it's an excellent Platinum Jubilee, or Platty Jube street party; whatever you want to call it. Good for you, Ivy'.

'It wasn't me; it was us', says Ivy.

'But we wouldn't have done it if you hadn't suggested it', says Ben.

'I love the Queen, and I wanted us to enjoy Her Majesty's special day with all of us together, as a community.'

'I worked at Buckingham Palace for a while', says Denise, 'and waited on Princess Margaret'.

'Denise told me all about it', says Ivy.

'I felt sorry for her, really', says Denise. 'Not really comfortable in her skin, was she?'

'No. Not happy with the role she was given', says Aoife.

'You can think of it as a workers' rights issue – The Royal Family', says Jed.

'I never thought of it like that', says Ben, 'not in those terms: workers' rights'.

'It puts a slightly different complexion on it', says Toby. 'This whole royal nonsense should be abolished.'

'For their own sake', says Aoife, 'and I'm not even going to start on that fecker, Andrew'.

'Let's not mention him today; I want to think nice thoughts about the Queen', says Denise.

'Fair point', says Aoife.

'So we should abolish the monarchy to put them out of their misery?' asks Ben.

'It's not fair on them, apart from anything else', says Toby, waving up to the cardboard Queen next to him. 'They could be cardboard cutouts, and still some people would hate them, some love them, just because of the family they were born into.'

The cardboard Queen waves back, smiling obliviously.

'We're all ghosts, existing in the imaginations of other people', says Aoife.

'That's deep', says Toby. 'Although, I get what you mean. To most people I'm just that bloke in the wheelchair, aren't I?'

'Exactly', says Aoife, 'when that's not really you at all, is it? Not the essence of you; the real you'.

'I don't think I fit my work role', says Nancy. 'I own a patisserie, and I don't eat cakes!'

'Bloody good ones!' says Toby, through a mouthful of cupcake.

'We can all change our careers, to some extent; the Royals can't', says Aoife. 'Even if one of them abdicates, they're still stuck with the family, and pursued by the media.'

'Now you mention it', says Toby, 'I remember Hils saying something about it being a contract of slavery. She did it in school in her Law A Level. No contract should amount to a contract of slavery; you have to be able to get out of it'.

'Where is she today; Hilary?' asks Aoife.

'A double shift on A&E', replies Toby. 'She couldn't get out of it', he says, grinning.

'It *does* seem toxic – the Royal Family', says Nancy, thoughtfully.

'I suppose', says Ivy, 'none of us choose to be born into the families we're given. But if it weren't for the Queen, we wouldn't be here today'.

Toby wipes a blob of purple buttercream icing from his mouth with his finger. 'We could have a national street party day; an annual bank holiday. We don't need the Royals to do it.'

'But just imagine; if we didn't have a royal family, our country's figurehead might be someone like... oh, lawks, like our "esteemed" prime minister, Boris.' There's a chorus of groans from everyone.

Stephen saunters over. 'We didn't need the umbrellas, in spite of the clouds.'

'Or our Rain-mates', says Nancy, with a giggle.

'A success then, all this?' says Jed.

'I think another success is you, stone cold sober, talking to a publican', says Toby. Jed smiles.

'Yeah, good for you', says Ben, punching Jed's shoulder as a sort of blokey equivalent of a hug.

'You were all correct', says Ivy, 'this is far better than my original idea. It's like a mosaic; the way the community fits together and makes something unique and colourful'.

'That sounds beautiful', says Bill. He's walked to Secret Street from his own street party in Sherwood, and is just arriving. He gives Ivy a hug, and a tender kiss on the lips.

'Oh, Ivy', says Nancy, 'you two; it's so romantic!'

'It's amazing what you can get on the internet these days', says Bill.

'You cheeky bugger!' says Ivy. 'Go and put the kettle on.' She points to her front door.

Above them, the bunting flips gently to and fro' in the light breeze. The colours – red, white, blue, and purple – stand out against the soft grey sky. Above the bunting, the finials on the tips of the gables point upward, as beneath them the residents transform from two rows of neighbours into a community of friends.

Eastbourne Promenade – Toby

The day of Her Majesty the Queen's funeral

Secret Street's always a nightmare for Toby on bin day; he can't get anywhere until the bins and boxes are all wheeled or carried back inside front gardens. The closest he gets to running is going as fast as he can in his wheelchair, but that's often impossible with people everywhere. Seafronts are good, though. Toby and Hilary come to Eastbourne quite often because Hilary likes the sea, and there's a long prom which means they can "walk" together, although Toby can't often get up much of a speed; it's normally busy here with day trippers and the like. Today it seems the entire world is either in London to see the funeral procession, or, like Hilary, at home watching it on TV. Toby doesn't go in for that royal malarkey. He knew the seafront would be quiet, so drove down here and it's empty, like a scene in a post-apocalyptic film. It's still quite sunny for September. He pushes his chair to get up speed, then lets go, and holds his arms out to the sides. Three miles of empty prom; just Toby and the seagulls, floating.

He can't see any shops open, but when they're in
Eastbourne, Hilary and Toby always go to a little
newsagent's on a road off the seafront by the bandstand, so
Toby reckons he'll try it. He crosses the empty road, wheels
round the corner, and it's open. He wheels adjacent to the
door, and pushes it open with his left hand. The bell on
the door tings as he steers himself in. Inside, there are no
other customers; no one to trip over his footplates. He can
see everything. He can reverse back to open the fridge and
get a Coke. He can see all the sweets. He never knew they
sold coconut ice; those long pink and white bars of it that
for some reason you get in seaside resorts. He picks one
up, and as he fishes his wallet out of his rucksack to pay,
the man behind the counter's been sitting there reading a
paperback.

'Not bothered about the funeral?' he asks.

'Nah', Toby replies, 'not my thing'.

The man waves his book at Toby. 'I've been meaning to
read this for months.'

Toby pays, the shopkeeper drops the change in his till,
pushes the till drawer shut, and says, 'Enjoy the rest of
the day'.

Toby wheels out of the shop into the sunshine, and
back to the prom. There's a slight incline from
the bandstand down to the end of the pathway at
Holywell, so he stops to put the coconut ice in his
rucksack, then aims his chair downwards, pushes as hard
and fast as he can, and lets go. He speeds down the path.
As the shopkeeper reads his book, Toby continues
whizzing, holding his arms out to the sides, feeling the
breeze through his fingers, as if the death of the Queen has
blessed them both with freedom for just one day.

96A Secret Street – Ivy Brown

Five months after the Platinum Jubilee street party

The sky outside is a dark sapphire blue, and it's Ivy's first night in her new flat. It had broken her heart – just a little bit – to close the front door on No. 11 for the last time, and take the keys down to the estate agents in the High Street. They'd advertised her house in *Executive Lifestyle Magazine*. That had made her laugh. It was sold to a Dr and Mrs Agarwal, but she knew nothing about them yet, and was hoping they would muck in with everyone else. Arthur said there was a Dr Agarwal at Pembury Hospital, so it might be him. 'He can resuscitate me if my team ever scores', Arthur said, laughing.

All Ivy's Secret Street friends had helped her pack and move in a hired Luton van. 'No need for a removal firm; we'll all turn to and help. Thrift, darling, thrift!' Beatrice had said. And they had, all of them, helped, either by loading and unloading the van, which Beatrice had skilfully shuttled up and down the hill, or by packing, or helping Ivy get rid of the furniture she no longer needed, either via the auction house, or to the British Heart Foundation second-hand furniture shop. Ivy had been glad to leave those fitted wardrobes behind.

As Ivy brushes her hair at her new bedroom window, Toby and Hils next door are watching *It's a Wonderful Life* on their DVD player. In the Otter, Stephen's clearing up after last orders. Across the road, Ian's asleep and dreaming of walking to a fountain with a stranger. Up the hill in the recovery house, a few of them chat in the living room, encouraging each other after the evening's therapy session. Others are in their rooms, watching TV, and wincing each time alcohol's mentioned as if life would be incomplete without it; in the bar as the TV detectives congratulate each other on finding the killer; in the adverts for Grouse whisky and Guinness. Across the road, Ben's dreading his probation officer's visit tomorrow, knowing she'll be trying to appear kind, but coming over as patronising. Four doors up, Aoife yells to the kids to turn down their music as she lies in bed reading a book about love, and hoping she hasn't passed on her old distrust of men to her daughter. Nancy's still out with her boyfriend in The Spice restaurant in Camden Road, and – just this once – to hell with the calories; she's having an Irish coffee. Across the road from Nancy's house, Lara's in bed asleep, but Aslan's still up, watching Premier League football, delaying bed time, afraid he'll have nightmares again. Next door, in the glow from the night light, Olivia checks Kismet's asleep, then runs to the bedroom where Fran's waiting for her, and jumps into their king-sized bed with a whoop. At the top of the hill, Beatrice is exhausted from driving the Luton – yanking its old-fashioned gear stick in and out of first gear – and is stirring her cocoa.

Outside Ivy's bedroom window, a silver crescent moon glints through the leafless branches of the oak trees at the back of the house. Her new garden's overgrown, and the fence a little tatty, but the shed in the far corner is in good condition and will be fine with a new coat of paint; sky blue, maybe. She thinks of all her new Secret Street friends. Apart from Stephen in the pub, they're now mostly up the hill from her, rather than down. She thinks how her own worries fade to nothing compared to others', and remembers Aslan's trauma reaction to dropping his cup on her rug. She still has the rug. It fits in her new living room just as well as it had in the old one, and she still has the sofas, because she needs them for all the people that come round for coffee these days – Columbian ground coffee, from Aldi. Right now 96A is a chaos of unpacked boxes and plastic carrier bags full of last-minute bits and bobs that were still lying around when the boxes were all full. Bill and Aslan have made sure her bedroom's organised, and her bed made up, so she can get a good night's sleep tonight.

She wonders what Mean Jean's doing now, and why she'd been a bully. She wonders what happened to the real Araminta Cavendish, and hopes she's had a good life. Ivy will be eighty-three next year. She might have two, three, even ten years left, but she doubts she has another fourteen and will live to be as old as the Queen. It's most likely this is the place she's going to die; not as Araminta, but as plain old, contented, Ivy Brown. She doesn't worry about dying. In the past it had terrified her, but now Ivy believes she's lived her life as well as anyone because she's known the extremes of emotion – toe-curling terror, fiery rage, deep, gnawing sadness, and pure joy – and therefore fully experienced what it is to be human. What's more, she's loved, and been loved, and surely that's enough on its own.

Ivy's still desperately sad that the Queen – her idol, her influence, her muse – only lived just over three months after Her Platinum Jubilee. She'll never forget watching the funeral on TV, hearing Big Ben toll ninety-six times; once for every year of Her Majesty's dutiful life. She'll never forget how the crown sparkled so brightly on top of that coffin. She'll never forget seeing Her Majesty's fell pony, Emma, brought out to pay her respects. There can't have been a dry eye in the country as people watched Emma flick her tail and stamp the ground with her hoof as the coffin passed slowly by on its way to lay the Queen to rest with her dear, departed husband, Philip, in the vaults of St. George's Chapel at Windsor Castle. And the corgis; those poor little dogs wondering where their mistress had gone, and when she'd be back. *Grief is the price we pay for love.*

Something moves in Ivy's garden. She gasps, she's so thrilled to see it: the old fox, the same one she's seen before, with the coat that looks sleek, yet moth-eaten. It seems to be settling down beneath the shed. As Ivy peers through the semi-darkness, she can see it looks as if it's hollowed out a den there. The fox stares across the garden at her. She's sure this time it catches her gaze. They regard each other. 'Hello again, old friend', she says, knowing it can't hear her through the double-glazed window, but hoping that, in some way, it can understand her. It curls itself into a ball, like a dog in a basket, with its face peeping out of the den's entrance below the shed. Slowly, tenderly, it closes its eyes. Ivy smiles to herself. She leaves the curtains open so she can still see the moon, replaces her hairbrush on the dressing table, and climbs into bed. As she turns out her bedside light, her heart feels peaceful, the stillness like velvet. Here, in the garden flat of 96 Secret Street, she's found her place at last, in the great untidy scheme of things, somewhere between executives and foxes.

THE END

Notes

All the stories in this book are based on truth. Some are pretty much told as they happened, others have been dramatized to blend with the narrative. In every case, the emotional truth has been scrupulously preserved. With one exception (Ian), the characters have been anonymised, and a few are a cut-and-shut of two people. Everybody involved is happy for their story to be used.

On chapter entitled '98A Secret Street: PC Toby "Chalky" White'

"...not using it for the purpose for which it was designed" is a line from a sketch called "Men's Talk" performed in 1976 by Alan Bennett and John Fortune as part of The Secret Policemen's Ball, a series of benefit shows to raise funds for Amnesty International.

On chapter entitled '65B Secret Street: Ian, the Old Barnardo's Boy'

In 2022, IICSA (the Independent Inquiry Into Child Sexual Abuse), published its report into historic abuse of boys shipped from Barnardo's homes to Canada and Australia, including 442 to Australia in the post-war period when Ian was in Barnardo's homes. The report states that Barnardo's sent boys there with the best of intentions, took reports of abuse seriously, took action to deal with it, and suspended their child migration programme as a result. The full report is available at the website referenced below. One of contemporary Barnardo's main aims is to prevent child abuse of all kinds and to support children who have suffered from it.

On Chapter entitled 'Darling, I think I'm about to disappear'

The quote from Kahlil Gibran is from *The Prophet*. The little light turquoise book was published by Collector's Library in 2011 and reissued by Pan Macmillan, London in 2016. ISBN: 978-1-909621-59-6

On Chapter entitled '19 Secret Street: Olivia'

If you're interested in further reading on finding meaning in distress, the author would hugely recommend *Man's Search for Meaning* by Viktor E. Frankl.

On chapter entitled '21 Secret Street: Aslan'

Pronunciation for Turkish words:

MIT – *mit* (pronounced as one word/syllable; like the English)

Milli İstihbarat Teşkilatı – sounds like *milly istifarat teshkil-lahta* şebeke – sounds like *shebekeh* (all with the "e" as in the English word, "shed")

Ali babanın bir çiftliği var – sounds like *ali barbarin beer chiftliggi var*

Mee! Mee! – *meh meh* (sheep sound; "e" as in "shed")

Hav! Hav! – *how how* (dog sound; similar to bow wow)

On chapter entitled 'The Platinum Jubilee Street Party'

The idea of the royal family as a workers' rights issue was not the author's original idea, but put to her by the Forward Prize-winning poet, Stephanie Sy-Quia, in the bar at the Contact Theatre, Manchester in 2022.

On chapter entitled '96A Secret Street: Ivy Brown'

'Grief is the price we pay for love' was said by Her Majesty Queen Elizabeth II in a message of support for the loved ones of the victims of the September 11th Twin Towers attacks in New York. It is allegedly taken from the book, *The Full Bereavement: Studies in Grief* (1972), by Colin Murray Parkes.

The book Aoife's reading is *We Need to Talk About Love* by Laura Mucha, published in 2020 by Bloomsbury Publishing PLC

References/Research

Along with online articles from newspapers and magazines far too numerous to mention, I am indebted to the creators of the following resources in the research for this book:

- Bradford, Sarah, *Queen Elizabeth II, Her Life in Our Times* (2012) Penguin Books
- Brown, Craig, *Ma'am, Darling, 99 Glimpses of Princess Margaret* (2017) Harper Collins, London
- Chapman, Frank, *Tales of Old Tunbridge Wells* (1999) Froglets Publications, Ltd, Westerham, Kent
- Farthing, Roger, *Royal Tunbridge Wells*, (1990) Phillimore & Co., Chichester
- Foreman, Don, *Royal Visitors to Tunbridge Wells* (1993) Parapress Limited, Tunbridge Wells
- Glenconner, Anne, *Lady in Waiting, My Extraordinary Life in the Shadow of the Crown* (2019) Hodder & Stoughton, London
- Hoey, Brian, *Not in Front of the Corgis* (2011) The Robson Press, London
- Lacey, Robert, *A Brief Life of the Queen* (2012), Duckworth Overlook, London
- Lumley, Joanna, *A Queen for all Seasons* (2021) Hodder & Stoughton, London

- Seward, Ingrid, *My Husband and I* (2017) Simon and Schuster, London
- Website: www.thecastlesofscotland.co.uk/the-best-castles/other-articles/comlongon-castle/
- Website: www.townandcountrymag.com/society/tradition/a3440/dr-roger-mugford-queen-elizabeth-ii-corgi-trainer-interview/
- YouTube: Prince Andrew & the Epstein Scandal: *The Newsnight Interview* – BBC News
- YouTube: *Prince Andrew & Epstein DECEPTION Body Language Revealed PART 1*
- YouTube: *Does Prince Andrew Lie? Epstein Interview Body Language Revealed PART 2*
- *Elizabeth & Margaret: Love and Loyalty.* TV documentary directed by Lucy Swingler and Stephanie Wessell
- *The Queenes welles: that is, a treatise of the nature and vertues of Tunbridge water*, 1632, Dr Lodwick Rowzee, Imprint: J. Dawson (From Tunbridge Wells library archives)
- https://www.barnardos.org.au/about-us/resources-child-abuse-neglect-in-Australia
- https://iicsa.org.uk/reports/recommendations/publications/investigation/child-migration/part-c-detailed-examination-institutional-responses/sending-institutions/barnardos

Acknowledgements

First and foremost, thanks are due to the contributors to this book, all but one of whose names have had to be anonymised, but who I now think of as Beatrice, Ben, Jed, Chalky, Minty, Stephen, Ian, Nancy, Aoife, Olivia and Aslan.

I would not have even started planning to write *Secret Street* if I hadn't suggested it, on a whim, to Mary Harris, and she had not replied, 'Yesss!', with such enthusiasm. Senior news reporter with local press, Mary has reported on Royal Tunbridge Wells for twenty-six years (and counting), writing with devotion about this town she loves. Mary is – and please forgive the cliché – the wind beneath *Secret Street*'s wings.

Sincere and heartfelt thanks are also due to:

- my longsuffering husband, Rob, for his willingness to engage in endless manuscript-related discussion, and for being my first beta reader.
- Beta readers Eileen Morrissey, Rob Moore, Miriam Sully, and Anika Carpenter.

- My kind, honest, generous, and knowledgeable mentors, John O'Donoghue and Hamish Ironside.
- Claire Dyer for her invaluable "Fresh Eyes" service, available from www.clairedyer.com.
- The poetry filmmaker, editor and writer, Helen Dewbery, for giving me an iPad when mine died. It was invaluable for recording and listening to contributors' interview transcripts, and creating the video for the Kickstarter campaign, which funded the printing of this first edition of the book. There's more info about Helen at poetryfilmlive.com.
- Ira Lightman for his mentoring in the early days of my poetry writing, which led to the creation of one of my favourite sentences in this book.
- Writers' HQ for their entertaining and effective writing courses and support: www.writershq.co.uk
- Tom Davis, Sonja Wright, Sarah Mitchell, and Tom Mortley, for willingly and cheerfully reading uncorrected proofs and giving *Secret Street* such thoughtful endorsements.
- Paul Macauley, for his astonishingly insightful and energy-boosting creativity coaching, available at www.paulmacauley.net

Patrons

You would not be reading this now if it were not for the following patrons who pledged to buy this special, limited, first edition hardback via a Kickstarter fundraiser that ran from the end of March to the end of April 2024.

These people understood that *Secret Street* is not about famous people or celebs; it's about all of us, and showed their support in a very real way by pledging to buy their own copy. To me, they will always be the original "Secret Streeters" (Sonja Wright's term), and all these names will always have a special place in my heart.

- Alan Hiron
- Alison Millis
- Angela and Dave Funnell
- Barry & Sam Fentiman-Hall – Wordsmithery
- The Burnell's
- Caroline Auckland
- Claire Armstrong
- Claire Dyer
- Craig Beeson & The Royal Oak team
- Ellen Morrissey
- Emma Goodwin

- Gilly, Taylor and Cali
- Graham Wilson and Judith Anderson
- Heidi Thomas
- Helen Mcloughlin
- Ian & Becky Patterson
- James Rands
- Jamie, Caroline, Ben & Sausage
- Jenny Bishop
- Josh Branch, TN1.gg
- Julian Altshul
- Julie
- Kirsty Farrow
- Lenka Urbankova
- Mick Canning
- Nathaniel Bradford
- Pamela Jane French
- Paul Macauley
- Paula Clarke
- Paula, Simon, Leo, Cody the dog, and Chase, the pussydog
- Phil O'Neill
- Ray & Clare, Lily & Ava Dhanowa
- Residents, TN1.gg
- Rob Campbell
- Rob Moore
- Roger Wood
- Sadie Hibbert
- Sally Strawberry
- Samantha Ayres
- Sarah Sabine
- Shan White – Ruby Tuesday Books
- Siobhan O'Connell

- Sophie Herxheimer
- Teresa & Stanley Banks, and June Cawley
- Tom Mortley
- Valerie Geddy
- Venetia Casely

Suggested Book Club
Discussion Points

1. As she talks to her neighbours, Araminta/Ivy learns about friendship. What do you think is the difference between an acquaintance and a friend?
2. Having read 'Secret Street', will you now be more likely to make friends among your neighbours?
3. The Tunbridge Wells portrayed in the book is very class-conscious. If you live in Tunbridge Wells, is this your experience? If elsewhere, do you think this is relevant to the place where you live? How does it manifest?
4. PC Chalky White believes northern police officers may not accept him because of his southern accent. Ben is relieved he wasn't sent to a northern jail. Olivia describes her ex-boyfriend as a 'typical northern bloke'. Do you think northerners really look down on southerners, and/or vice versa?
5. Jed's childhood clearly had an enormous effect on him, but how much – if at all – do you feel his addiction and homelessness are his fault?
6. Beatrice's son, Hugo, and his wife, Lucy have decided not to have children because of the likelihood of them

inheriting a tendency to addiction. Are they right to make this decision, or are they being overly cautious?

7. Do you think that people talking openly about their own psychosocial issues such as addiction, or mental health problems, reduces stigma?

8. It's easy to look back on the stigma of having a child out of wedlock as outdated and unnecessarily damning, yet some secrets in the book remain untold (Olivia's child, Kismet, being born of rape; Nancy's abortion; Hugo's cocaine addiction; Aslan's asylum seeking). Is society just as unaccepting today as it was when these characters experienced their traumas?

9. After #MeToo, I really shouldn't have been, but I was surprised about the number of times sexual violence against women cropped up in the stories (Ben's stepdaughter, Olivia's boyfriend, Aoife's childhood). Do you think this is something that will always be prevalent in our society, or are things improving?

10. There is currently disagreement in society about asylum seekers and a great deal of ignorance about what is and isn't legal. If you had been the judge deciding his case, would you have granted Aslan Indefinite Leave to Remain?

11. Councillor Petty is portrayed as a pompous, mansplaining "Captain Mainwaring". Is this fair? What is his motivation? Do women 'splain as much as men?

12. Many of the characters' problems arose in childhood and were related to their parents being unhappy. What implications might this have as to whether unhappy couples should "stay together for the sake of the kids"?

13. "Pensioners" are routinely portrayed by the media as bent double, shuffling along with a Zimmer frame in a nursing home. Were you surprised that Minty is eighty-two, yet drives, does aerobics, uses a dating app, and goes to the pub on her own? If so, why? Can you think of any instances of ageism? Have you witnessed, or experienced it?

About the cover artist, Elaine Gill

The cover illustration for *Secret Street* was created by celebrated Tunbridge Wells artist, Elaine Gill. Elaine read *Secret Street* twice, slowly absorbing and reflecting on the stories, before coming up with the perfect design to evoke the feeling of the book.

Elaine is perhaps best known for her illustrated maps, and takes commissions from organisations including the National Trust. Her map of Tunbridge Wells is displayed on the wall in The Amelia Scott Centre, Tunbridge Wells. Elaine was also involved in the creation of the mural on Platform One of Tunbridge Wells Railway Station.

You can find more about Elaine and her unique commissions, *Your Story Illustrated,* at www.elainegill.co.uk.